Sing Nowell

and

arranged

NOVELLO & COMPANY LTD 160 WARDOUR STREET, LONDON W.1

This collection of carols
is produced under the editorship of
LOUIS HALSEY & BASIL RAMSEY

A selection of fourteen carols from Sing Nowell *is recorded on ARGO RG399 (Mono) and ZRG5399 (Stereo) by the Elizabethan Singers under the direction of Louis Halsey, with Simon Preston (organ).*

MUSIC CALIGRAVED AT THETFORD, NORFOLK,
BY CALIGRAVING LTD
PRINTED AND BOUND IN ENGLAND BY THE
HOLLEN STREET PRESS, LONDON W.1

Preface

In this book we have tried to produce a mid-twentieth-century collection of the best in contemporary British carol writing and arrangement. In a few cases we have made use of recently-published material, but our chief purpose has been to encourage composers to write new pieces or to make fresh arrangements of traditional carols which, for one reason or another, will always be sung. We have included as many important British composers of our generation as possible.

Every effort has been made to keep the carols within the capabilities of a reasonably proficient choir. Although this restriction can prove troublesome to composers, we have felt justified in relaxing it only where musical worth clearly overrides all other considerations. We believe, however, that very few carols in this book present a really formidable challenge.

The performing notes at the end of each carol are intended to save the choirmaster's time by indicating likely trouble spots and giving interpretative hints. They can, of course, be disregarded. Similarly, the metronome marks are for guidance only. Bar numbers, for convenience during rehearsal, are given beneath the beginning of each stave.

LOUIS HALSEY
BASIL RAMSEY

Contents

Where carol titles differ from the opening words, both are indexed. The abbreviations (for Annunciation, Advent, Christmas, St Stephen, Holy Innocents, New Year, & Epiphany) indicate the season for which carols are particularly suited.

I

A Babe is born

Words
15th CENTURY

Music
PETER RACINE FRICKER
(1962)

day Ve - ni Cre - a - tor Spi - ri - tus. At
Ve - ni Cre - a - tor Spi - ri - tus.
Ve - ni Cre - a - tor Spi - ri - tus. At
Ve - ni Cre - a - tor Spi - ri - tus.
8
Beth - le - hem, that bles - sèd place, The child of bliss now
O lux, O lux
Beth - le - hem, that bles - sèd place, The child of bliss now
O lux, O lux
12

born he was: And him to serve God gave us
be - a - ta,
born he was: And him to serve God gave us
be - a - ta,
16
grace, O lux be - a - ta Tri - ni - tas.
O lux be - a - ta Tri - ni - tas.
mf
grace, O lux be - a - ta Tri - ni - tas. There
mf
O lux be - a - ta Tri - ni - tas. There
mf
19

mf
A so - lis, A so -
mf
A so - lis, A so -
came three kings out of the east, To wor - ship the king that
came three kings out of the east, To wor - ship the king that
23
- lis or - tus,
- lis or - tus,
is so free, With gold and myrrh and fran - kin -
is so free, With gold and myrrh and fran - kin -
27

A so - lis or - tus car - di - ne.
A so - lis or - tus car - di - ne. The
cense, A so - lis or - tus car - di - ne. The
cense, A so - lis or - tus car - di - ne.
30
Jam or - tus, Jam or -
shep - herds heard an an - gel's cry, A mer - ry song then
shep - herds heard an an - gel's cry, A mer - ry song then
Jam or - tus, Jam or -
34

- tus so - lis,
sun - gen he. 'Why are ye so sore a -
sun - gen he. 'Why are ye so sore a -
- tus so - lis,
p
p
38
f
Jam or - tus so - lis car - di - ne. The
ghast?' Jam or - tus so - lis car - di - ne. The
ghast?' Jam or - tus so - lis car - di - ne. The
Jam or - tus so - lis car - di - ne. The
ff
f
41

an - gels came down with one cry, A mer - ry
an - gels came down with one cry, A mer - ry
an - gels came down with one cry, A mer - ry
an - gels came down with one cry, A mer - ry
45

p
song then sun - gen they In the wor - ship of that child:
p
song then sun - gen they In the wor - ship of that child:
p
song then sun - gen they In the wor - ship of that child:
p
song then sun - gen they In the wor - ship of that child:
p
48

Allow the melody to stand out from wherever it is placed in the texture. Reflect the music's increasing intensity and make the last verse bold and exciting. Use a legato, flowing style, except in the Latin refrains.

A Child this day is born

Words
TRADITIONAL

Music arr. by
DAVID BARLOW
English tune

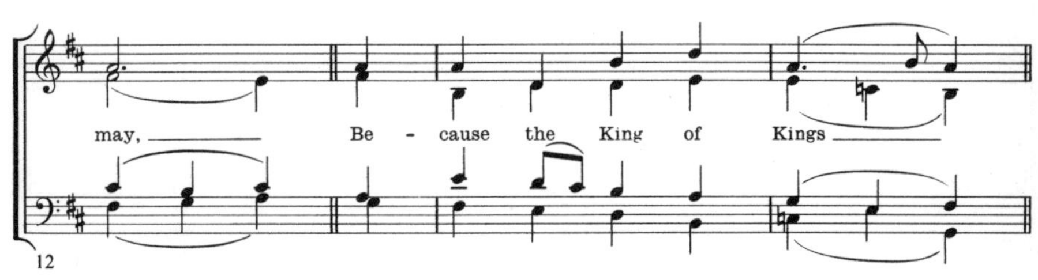

mp
No - el, No - el, No - el, No -
2 These ti - dings shep - herds heard Whilst watch-ing o'er their fold; 'Twas
mf
19
el, No-el, No-el, No-el, No-el, No-el, No - el.
by an An - gel un - to them That night re - vealed and told.
23
REFRAIN
REFRAIN (after vv. 2 & 4)
Glad ti - dings to all men, Glad ti - dings sing we
27
may, Be - cause the King of kings
30
Was born on Christ - mas Day.
f
3 Then was there with the
33

* immediately

Bright, with flowing quavers, particularly in the accompaniments. Avoid a stodgy four-in-the-bar feeling. The big leaps in the second part of the tune should be taken carefully. Let verses and refrains run smoothly into each other without lengthy gaps

3

A Shepherd's Carol

pinkie = finger   horse opera = Western

*By permission of the Author.

Tempo I
S
A
CHORUS O lift your lit - tle pin - kie, and
T
B
pp
ten.
14
touch the win - ter sky.
Love's all o - ver the
più f
16
mountains where the beau - ti - ful go to die.
dim.
19
TENOR SOLO
Allegretto
p con eleganza
2 If I were a Va - len - tine, and For - tune were a broad, I'd
22
espress.
dim.
pp leggiero
26 hyp - no-tise that ice - berg till she kissed me of her own ac - cord - O.
Tempo I
CHORUS O lift your lit - tle pin - kie, and
30

touch the win - ter sky.
Love's all o - ver the
mountains where the beau - ti - ful go to die.
ALTO SOLO
Vivace
pesante e giocoso
3 If I'd stacked up the vel - vet and my crook-ed rib were dead, I'd be
breed - ing white ca - na - ries and eat - ing crack-ers in bed - O.
rall.
Tempo I
CHORUS O lift your lit - tle pin - kie, and
touch the win - ter sky.
Love's all o - ver the

The solos should be well characterized, whilst the choruses need delicate and unhurried singing.

4

Adam lay ybounden

Words
ANON, 15th century

Music
BORIS ORD

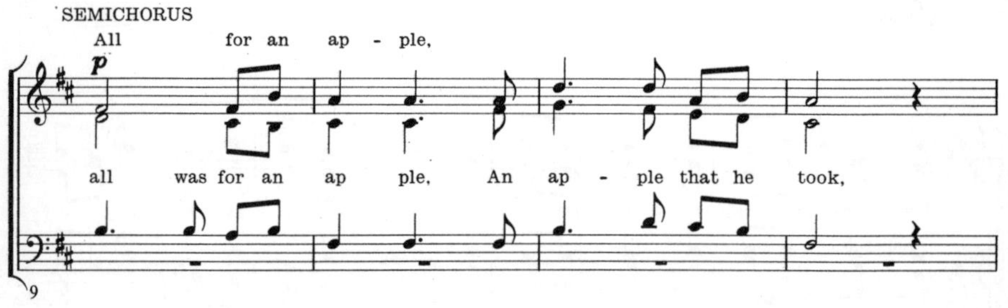

* = must

Use a simple, narrative style increasing in intensity until the last verse. Nothing less than four-bar phrases, singing very smoothly.

5

An Australian Carol

(Nativity)

Words
JAMES McAULEY*

Music
MALCOLM WILLIAMSON

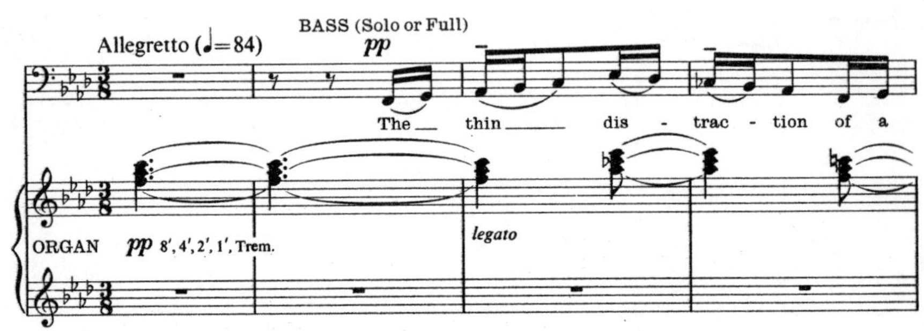

* Words from 'A Vision of Ceremony', by permission of Angus & Robertson Ltd.

The S and B sections may be taken by soloists. If not, use only B's with good, comfortable low notes, otherwise the line will sound muddy; like wise S's with clear, light voices who can end a phrase quietly on top *A*♭. Both words and music call for delicate treatment.

6

A Virgin most pure

Words
TRADITIONAL

Music arr. by
BRIAN BROCKLESS
English tune

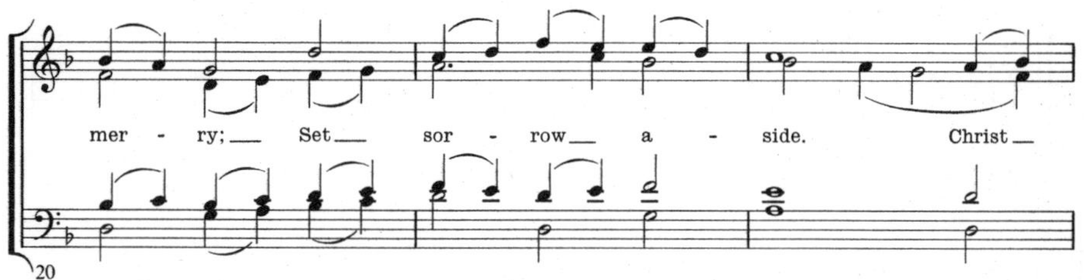

1 A Virgin most pure, as the Prophets do tell,
Hath brought forth a Baby, as it hath befell;
To be our Redeemer from Death, Hell, and Sin,
Which Adam's trangression had wrappèd us in.
Aye, and therefore, *etc.*

2 In Bethlehem Jewry a City there was,
Where Joseph and Mary together did pass,
And there to be taxèd with many a one mo,
For Caesar commanded the same should be so.

3 But when they had entered the City so fair,
A number of people so mighty was there,
That Joseph and Mary, whose substance was small,
Could find in the Inn there no lodging at all.

verses 4—7 on p. 23

S
A
T
B
4
7
10
13

REFRAIN

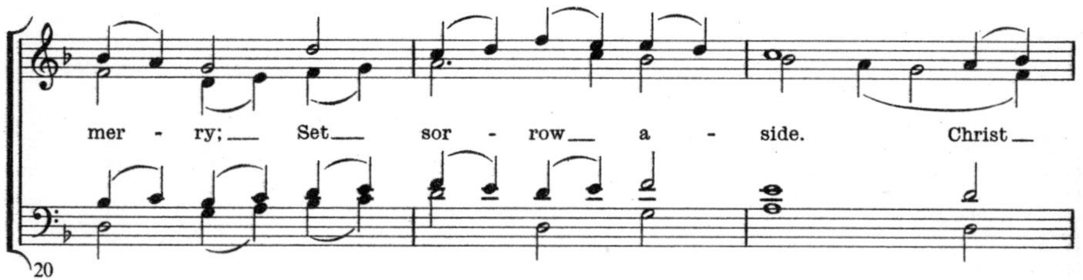

4 Then they were constrained in the stable to lye,
Where horses and asses they used for to tie;
Their lodging so simple they took it no scorn,
But against the next morning our Saviour was born.

5 The King of all kings to this world being brought,
Small store of fine linen to wrap Him was sought;
And when she had swadled her young Son so sweet,
Within an ox manger she laid Him to sleep.

6 Then God sent an Angel from Heaven so high,
To certain poor shepherds in fields where they lye,
And bade them no longer in sorrow to stay,
Because that our Saviour was born on this day.

7 Then presently after the shepherds did spy
A number of Angels that stood in the sky;
They joyfully talkèd and sweetly did sing,
'To God be all glory our Heavenly King'.

The melody has been embellished rather in the manner of a chorale. V. 1 can be sung as an unaccompanied solo (S or T). Use the alternative version for vv. 3 and 6 if T can bring the tune clearly through the surrounding texture without strain. Adopt a tempo that does not hurry the passing notes.

7

Angels from the realms of glory

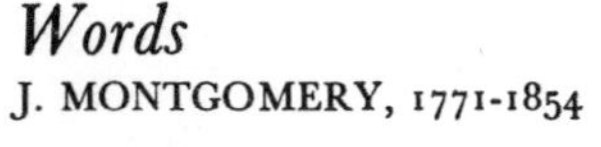

Words
J. MONTGOMERY, 1771-1854

Music arr. by
ARTHUR OLDHAM
French tune

Allegretto (♩=116)

REFRAIN

in
- - - - ri - a in ex - cel - sis De - - o,
17

2 Shep - herds in the field a-bid - ing, Watch - ing o'er your flocks by night,
2 Shep - herds a - bid - ing, Watch - ing by night,
22

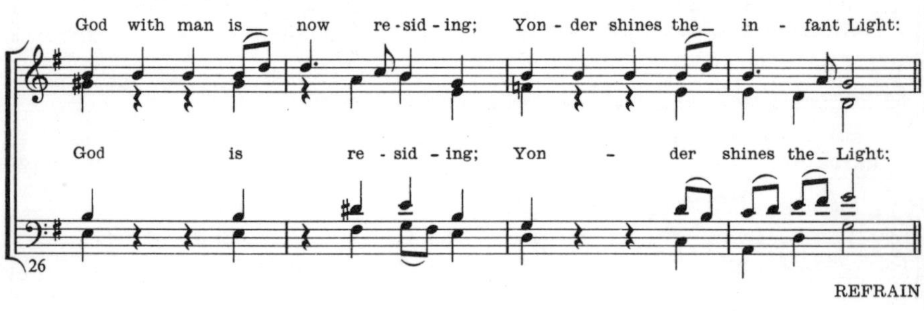
God with man is now re - sid - ing; Yon - der shines the in - fant Light:
God is re - sid - ing; Yon - der shines the Light;
26
REFRAIN

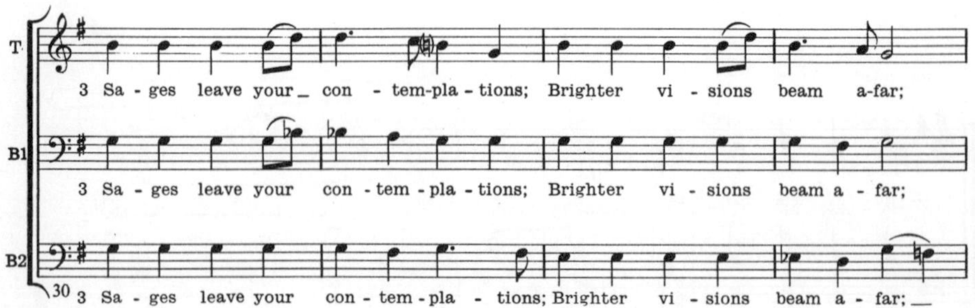
T
3 Sa - ges leave your con - tem-pla - tions; Brighter vi - sions beam a-far;
B1
3 Sa - ges leave your con - tem - pla - tions; Brighter vi - sions beam a - far;
B2
30
3 Sa - ges leave your con - tem - pla - tions; Brighter vi - sions beam a - far;

Slight modifications to the tune have brought it in line with the original version. Aim here for lightness and a tempo that avoids undue haste. Points to watch: T climb to *G* in vv. 1 and 2, ATB attack in v. 2, and BI balance in v. 3.

REFRAIN (Tempo I)

8

Angelus ad Virginem

Words
EARLY ENGLISH
(Modernized by Raymond Warren)

Music arr. by
RAYMOND WARREN
English tune

Gently flowing and espressive (♩ = 60)

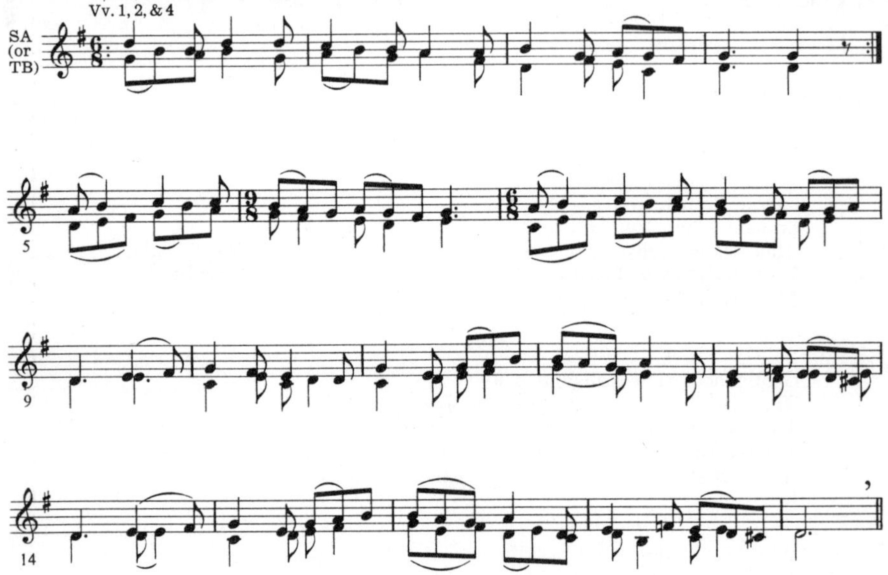
Vv. 1, 2, & 4
SA
(or
TB)
5
9
14

A little slower, more formal (♩ = 50)

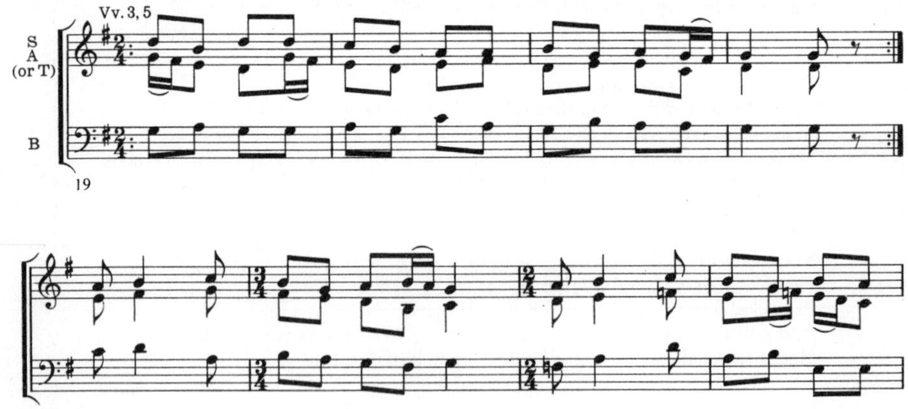
Vv. 3, 5
S
A
(or T)
B
19
23
27

1

Gabriel, from heaven's king sent to the maiden sweetë,
Brought to her blissful tiding and fair he 'gan her greetë:
'Hale be thou, full of grace aright. For God's own Son, that heavenly light,
For human love will human prove, receiving his flesh from maiden bright
Thereby mankind retrieving from sin and devil's might'.

2

Gently then the maiden mild to answer him begannë:
'How shall I conceive a child, a maid without a mannë?'
Then said the angel: 'Fear thou naught: by th' Holy Ghost it shall be wrought,
This selfsame thing whereof I bring thee tiding. Mankind by sin distraught
In thy sweet Son confiding shall out of pain be brought'.

3

When the maiden understood the word the angel toldë,
Mildly she, in gentle mood, her answer did unfoldë:
'Handmaiden of the Lord I wis, am I that have been raised to this;
Within my breast God's high behest is criéd since now I know it is
His will that maid unmarried shall have a mother's bliss'.

4

Th' angel went away anon and vanished from here sightë,
And her womb did stir full through the Holy Ghost his mightë.
In her the seed of Christ was sown, true God, true man in flesh and bone,
Whose life on earth a human birth did borrow. Through him good hope is own
Since on the cross in sorrow for us he did atone.

5

Maiden mother, spotless quite, with milk thy bosom filléd,
Plead for mercy on our plight, till our worst fears be stilléd.
Pray God forgive us for thy sake and clean of ev'ry guilt us make,
And grant us bliss when our time is for dying. With life above at stake
Here with God's will complying, that he to him us take.

Give the two-part version to soloists or semichorus with full chorus in the three-part version, or use one version throughout, perhaps omitting v. 4. Keep the quavers (first version) and semiquavers (second version) even.

9

Away in a manger

lay. the — lit - tle Lord Je - sus a - sleep in the
19
S
hay. the ba - by a -
A
The cat - tle are low - ing, — the
T
The cat - tle are — low - ing, the — ba - by a -
B
The — cat - tle are low - ing, the
mp
mf
23
Ped. (8′)
wakes, but Lord Je - sus no cry - ing He makes.
ba - by a - wakes, but Lord Je - sus no cry - ing He makes, I —
wakes, but — lit - tle Lord Je - sus no — cry - ing He makes, I
ba - by a - wakes, but Lord Je - sus — no — cry - ing He — makes.
27

Lord Je - sus, look down from the
love thee, Lord Je - sus! O stay
love thee, Lord Je - sus, look down from the sky and
Lord Je - sus, look down from the sky and
32
p
sky and stay by my cra - dle.
p pp
by my cra - dle. Be
stay by my cra - dle till morn - ing is nigh.
dim. p
stay by my cra - dle till morn - ing is nigh.
p pp
36 Man.

mf
Be near me, Lord
mf
near me, Lord Je - sus, Be near me, Lord
mf
Be near me, Lord
mf
Be near me, Lord
40
Ped. (16′, 8′)
Je - sus; I ask thee to stay close by me for
Je - sus; I ask thee to stay close by me for
Je - sus; I ask thee to stay close by me for
Je - sus; I ask thee to stay close by me for
8′, 4′
mf
45

rinf
ev - er, and love me, I pray! Bless all the dear
ev - er, and love me, I pray! Bless all the dear
ev - er, and love me, I pray! Bless all the dear
ev - er, and love me, I pray! Bless all the dear
49
child - ren in thy ten - der care, and fit us for
child - ren in thy ten - der care, and fit us for
child - ren in thy ten - der care, and fit us for
child - ren in thy ten - der care, and fit us for
53

Avoid needless sentimentality; the tune has its own charm. Points to watch: A should cover *C* in bar 31, T sing lightly in bars 44-47, and all parts stagger breathing in last 6 bars.

10

Balulalow

Words
JAMES, JOHN & ROBERT WEDDERBURN

Music
LOUIS HALSEY

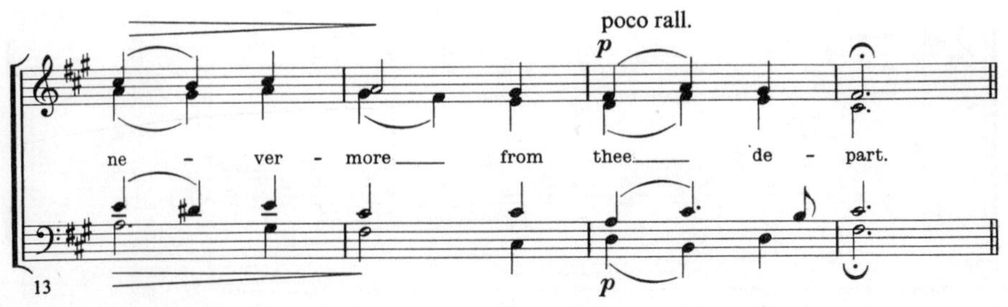

*spreit = spirit (pron. *spreet*)

*gloir = glory (pron. *glor*)

Sing with a gentle lilt and legato flow. Think in four-bar phrases (i.e. no breath after 'heart', bar 2), and ensure neatness at phrase-ends.

11

Blessed be that maid Mary

Words
OLD ENGLISH
(*Modernized by G. R. Woodward*)*

Music arr. by
LOUIS HALSEY
English tune

*From the Cowley Carol Book by permission of A. R. Mowbray & Co. Ltd.

S
A
p
p
3 Sweet and bliss - ful was the song
13
Chan - ted of the an - gel throng. "Peace on earth", Al -
15
le - lu - ya, In ex - cel - sis glo - ri - a.
18
mf
E - ya! Je - sus ho - di - e
21
mf
Na - tus est de vir - gi - ne.
23

A
T
B
mp
4 Fare three Kings from far - off land, Incense, gold, and myrrh in hand:
mf
25 mp

In Beth-lem the Babe they see
Stel - le duc - ti lu - mi - ne.
29

mf
E - ya! Je - sus ho - di - e Na - tus est de vir - gi - ne.
f
33 mf

5 Make we mer - ry on this fest, In quo Christ - us
S
A
f
5 Make we mer - - ry, In quo Christ - us
5 Make we mer - ry, In quo Christ - us
T
B
37
f
5 Make we mer - ry, Christ - us

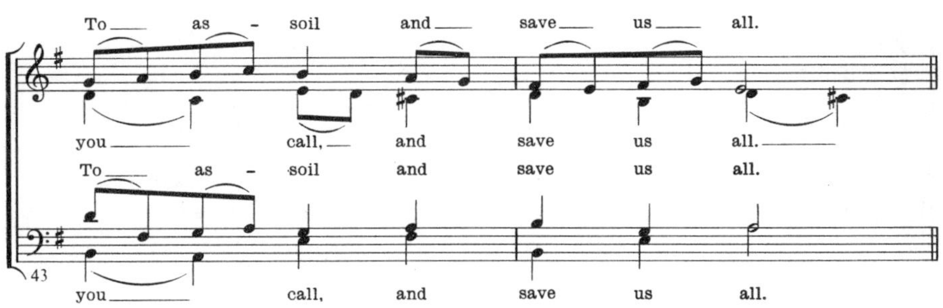

Can be performed as set, or as follows: (*a*) all verses sung to music of vv. 1 and 2, (*b*) vv. 1, 2, 3 and 4 to music of v. 1, and v. 5 to its own setting, (*c*) as set, with vv. 3 and 4 taken by solo voices. Take care with note values at phrase ends. If A need help with top *E* towards end of v. 5, add a S or two for the last 7 bars.

Ding dong! merrily on high

Words
G. R. WOODWARD*

Music arr. by
MALCOLM WILLIAMSON
French tune

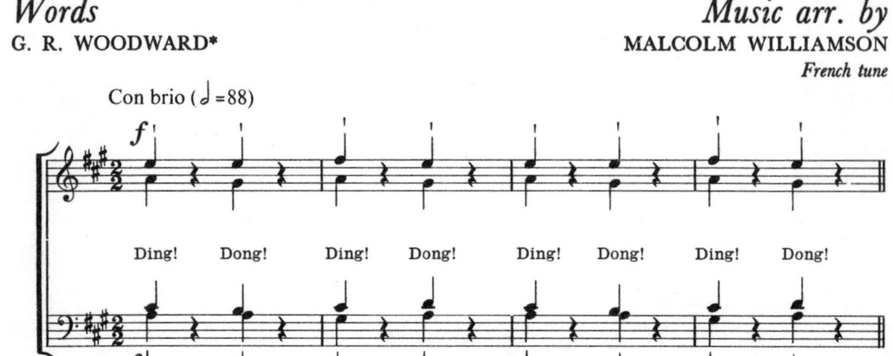

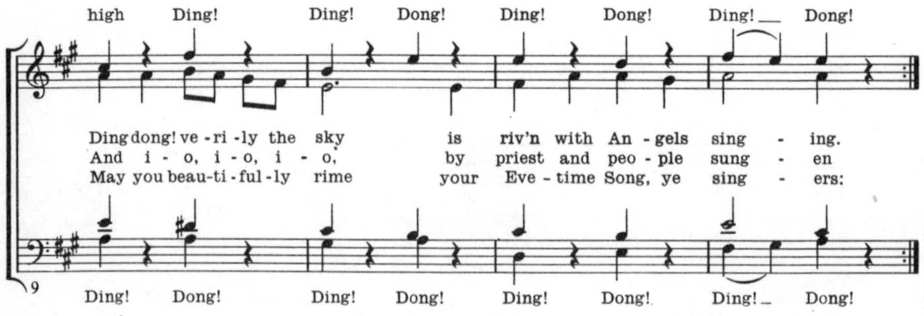

*From the Cambridge Carol Book by permission of the S.P.C.K.

The A line in the verses can be stiffened with a S or two and the punctuating STB chords must be rhythmically precise. The A tune should be carefully shaped. S must avoid a lumpy four-in-the-bar feeling in the refrain.

13

Eastern Monarchs

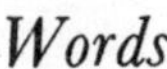

Words
LATIN, 15th century
(*English translation anon*)

Music
PETER NAYLOR

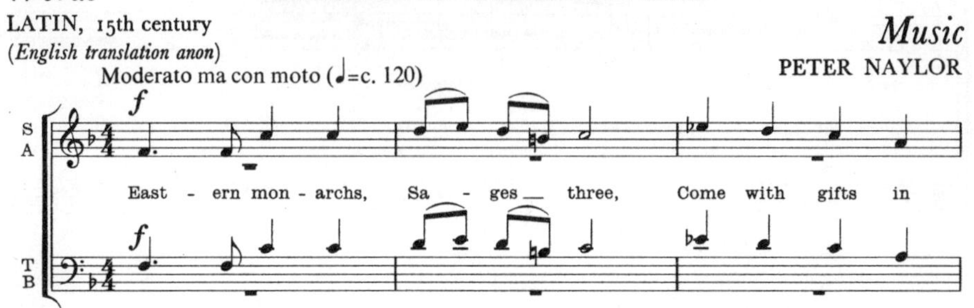

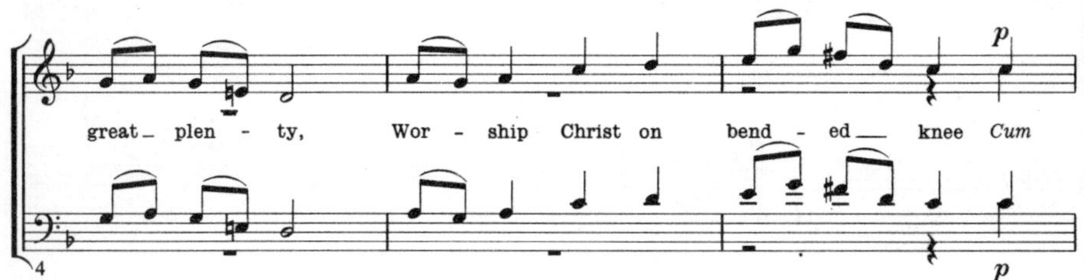

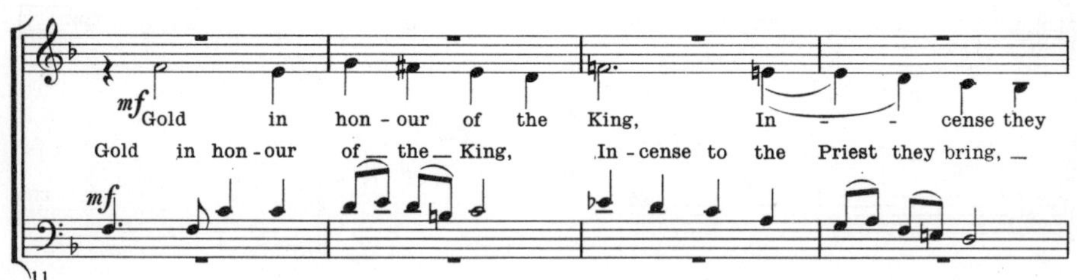

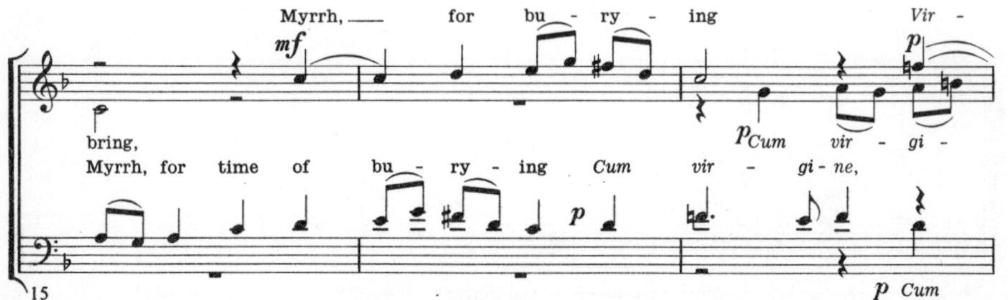

Precise (particularly in opening unison passage), bright, and not markedly smooth, except with the Latin words.

14

Ecce Puer

Words
JAMES JOYCE*

Music
BERNARD NAYLOR

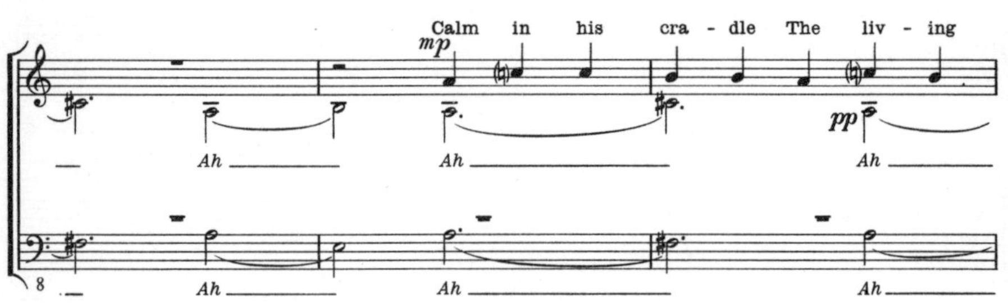

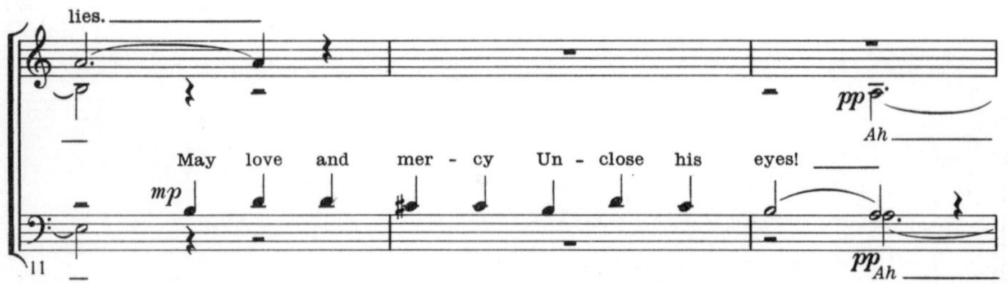

*By permission of the Society of Authors as the literary representative of the Estate of the late James Joyce

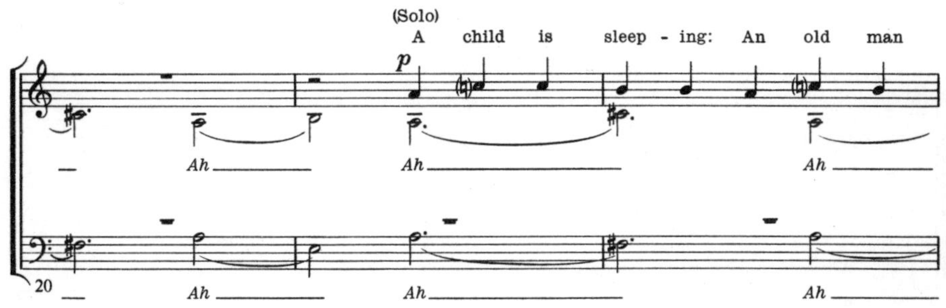

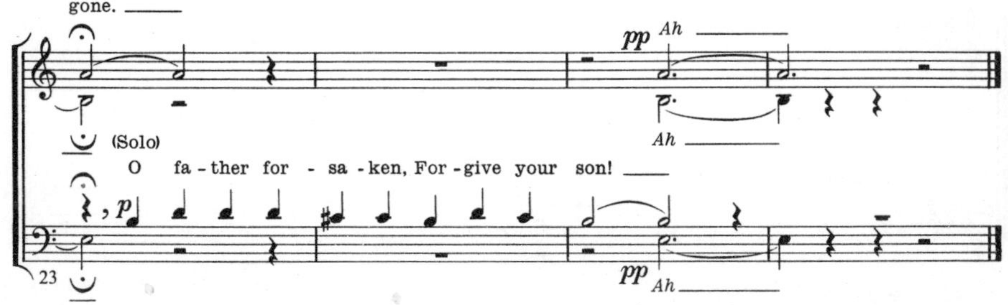

The 3-3-2-2 rhythmic scheme should be treated easily and delicately, with the melody given suitable prominence. Ensure that each melodic phrase is picked up quickly.

15

Dormi, Jesu

Words
TRADITIONAL
(*English translation by Peter Aston*)

Music
PETER ASTON

English words Publisher's copyright

Smooth and simple. Crescendos must not be out of proportion to the size of the piece.

16

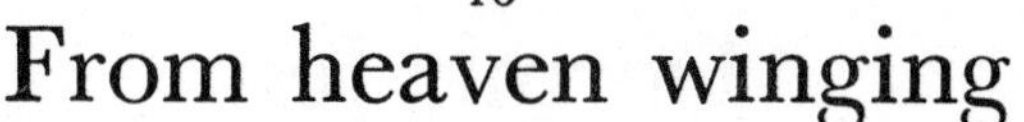

From heaven winging

Words
GERMAN TRADITIONAL
(*English translation by Laurence Swinyard*)*

Music arr. by
BASIL RAMSEY
Hungarian tune

Andante semplice

S A / T B: *mf*

From heav-en wing-ing, an-gels are sing-ing

Andante semplice (♩=96)

ORGAN: *p* (*reed tone*)

Shep-herds hark! *p* (*echo*) Shep-herds hark! *mf* Bring-ing glad ti-ding,

Good-will a-bi-ding Shep-herds hark! Shep-herds hark!

p (*flutes*)

*Words Publisher's copyright

SOPRANO (Solo or Full)
p
Your flocks for - sak - ing, staff in hand ta - king,
10
(echo)
Shep - herds haste! Shep - herds haste! Hast - en where yon - der,
13
waits the world's Won - der, Shep - herds haste! Shep - herds haste!
16
mf
Crad - led so low - ly, Ba - by so ho - ly,
mf
(Accomp. ad lib.)
19

Two-bar phrases and expressive singing. Watch the leap from *B* to *E* each time it occurs. Avoid hurrying the quavers.

17

God rest you merry, gentlemen

Words
TRADITIONAL

Music arr. by
JOHN JOUBERT

had long time gone a - stray, And it's ti - dings of com - fort and
14
joy, Comfort and joy, And it's ti - dings of com - fort and
18
SOPRANO(Full)
mf
2 From God that is our
joy.
dim.
p
22

Fa - ther The bles - sed An - gels came, Un - to some cer - tain
26
Shep - herds With ti - dings of the same; That there was born in
30
Beth - le - hem, The Son of God by name. And it's ti - dings of
34
com - fort and joy, comfort and joy, And it's ti - dings of
38

ALTO(Full)
mf
com - fort and joy.
3 Go, fear not, said God's
Man.
p legato
An - gels Let no - thing you af - fright,
For there is born in
Beth - le - hem, Of a pure Vir - gin bright,
One a - ble to ad -
vance you, And threw down Sa - tan quite,
And it's ti - dings of

com - fort and joy, com fort and joy, And it's ti - dings of
com - fort and joy.
TENOR (Full) mf
4 The Shep - herds at those
mp
ti - dings Re - joi - cèd much in mind, And left their flocks a -
feed - ing In tem - pest storms of wind, And strait they came to

Beth - le - hem, The son of God to find. And it's ti - dings of
74
com - fort and joy, comfort and joy, And it's ti - dings of
78
com - fort and joy.
BASS(Full) mf 5 Now when they came to
mf
82
Beth - le - hem Where our sweet Sa - viour lay, They found him in a
86

man - ger Where ox - en feed on hay, The bles - séd Vir - gin
90
knee - ling down Un - to the Lord did pray. And it's ti - dings of
94
com - fort and joy, com fort and joy, And it's ti - dings of
98
SOPRANO p
ALTO
6 With sud - den joy and
TENOR
com - fort and joy.
BASS p
6 With
p
102

glad - ness The shep - herds were be - guil'd, To see the Babe of
106
sud - den joy and glad - ness The shep - herds were be - guil'd, To

Is - ra - el Be - fore his mo - ther mild, On them with joy and
110
see the Babe of Is - ra - el Be - fore his Mo - ther mild, On

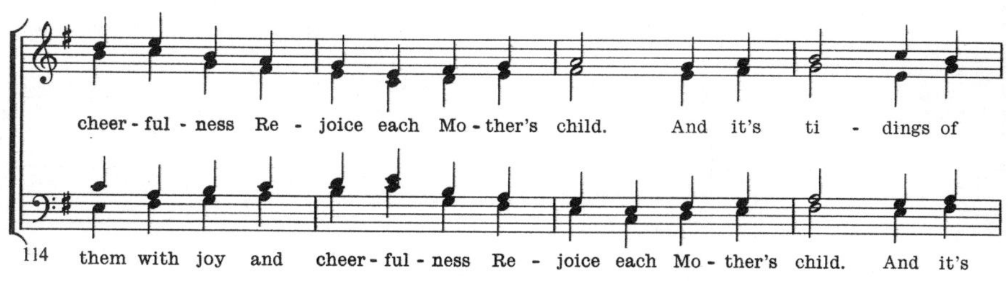
cheer - ful - ness Re - joice each Mo - ther's child. And it's ti - dings of
114
them with joy and cheer - ful - ness Re - joice each Mo - ther's child. And it's

com - fort and joy, comfort and joy, And it's ti - dings of
118
ti - dings of com - fort and joy, comfort and joy, And it's

com - fort and joy.
ti - dings of com - fort and joy.
mp cresc.
122
Ped.
f
7 Now to the Lord sing prai - ses All you with - in this
7 Now to the Lord sing prai - ses All
mf
126
place, Like we true lov - ing Breth - ren, Each o - ther to em -
you with - in this place, Like we true lov - ing Breth - ren, Each
130

brace, For the mer - ry time of Christ - mas Is draw - ing on a -
o - ther to em - brace, For the mer - ry time of Christ - mas Is
134
pace. And it's ti - dings of com - fort and joy, comfort and
draw - ing on a - pace. And it's ti - dings of com - fort and
138
joy, And it's ti - dings of com - fort and joy.
joy, comfort and joy, And it's ti - dings of com - fort and
142

ff
8 God bless the ru - ler
joy.
ff
ff
146
of this House, And send him long to reign, And ma-ny a mer - ry
150
Christ - mas May live to see a - gain. A - mong your friends and
154

Treat as a swinging two-in-the-bar with care for the shape of the tune. V. 3 for the A may present problems but is worth the effort, even with stiffening from a S or two. In vv. 6 and 7, rehearse SA and TB separately so that flow and phrasing do not suffer when the parts meet in canon.

18

Good King Wenceslas

Though the frost was cru - el, When a poor man came in sight, Gath'-ring win-ter fu -
8
THE SAINT(Bass)
mf
Hi - ther, page, and stand by me, If thou know'st it, tel - ling,
el.
p 8' Reeds
11
Yon - der pea - sant, who is he? Where and what his dwel - ling?
15
THE PAGE(Soprano)
mf
Sire, he lives a good league hence, Un - der - neath the moun - tain,
19

Right a - gainst the fo - rest fence, By Saint Ag - nes' foun - - tain.
23
THE SAINT
p
Bring me flesh, and bring me wine, Bring me pine - logs hi - ther.
8′Fl.
27
Man.
Thou and I will see him dine, When we bear them thi - ther.
31
THE NARRATORS
p
Ah
Page and mon - arch forth they went, Forth they went to - ge - ther;
mf
p
Ah
8′& 2′Fl.,Tierce
35
Ped.

Ah

Through the rude wind's wild la - ment, And the bit - ter wea - -

Ah

37

mp THE PAGE

Sire, the night is dark - er now,

Ah

mf

Page and mon - arch forth they went, Forth they went to - ge - ther;

ther. Ah

p

Ah

39

And the wind blows stron - ger, Fails my heart, I

Ah Ah

cresc.

Through the rude wind's wild la-ment, And the bit - ter wea - ther, Ah

Ah Ah

cresc.

Ah Ah

41

know not how; I can go no long - er.
f THE SAINT
Mark my foot-steps,
Ah
dim.
Ah
Ah
Ah
dim.
Ah
44
good my page; Tread thou in them bold - ly; Thou shalt find the
mp
In his mas-ter's steps he trod,
mp
L.H.
p
48
win - ter's rage Freeze thy blood less
Where the snow lay din - ted; Heat was in the ve - ry sod
52

Treat as a drama involving two actors, with the chorus providing the narration and pointing the moral at the end. The chorus must give the words time to breathe when the tune is sung in quavers, and avoid excessive intrusion when accompanying the soloists. Bring out the colour: the high organ thirds representing falling snow, the Saint's dignified manner (emphasized by the organ chords), the chromatic background to the Page's fears, and so on.

19

Here we bring new water

Words
ANON

Music
BERNARD NAYLOR

The sev'n bright gold wires
wa - ter and the wine.
The sev'n bright gold
The sev'n bright gold wires
The sev'n bright gold
f
13
wires
and the bu - gles that do shine.
wires
f
f marcato
Ped.
17
Sing reign of Fair Maid, with gold up-on her toe,
f
f (Sw.)
21

O - pen you the West Door, and turn the Old Year go.
25
Sing reign of Fair Maid, with gold up-on her chin,
(Sw.)
(Gt.)
(Sw.)
29
O - pen you the East Door, and let the New Year in.
(Sw.)
Gt.
(Sw.)
33

The S and B sections may be taken by soloists. The three-note ascending and descending figures on the organ connect the vocal phrases and introduce new keys. See that the voices and organ flow into each other easily.

20

Infant holy

Words
POLISH TRADITIONAL
(*English translation by Edith M. Reed*)

Music arr. by
EDMUND RUBBRA
Polish tune

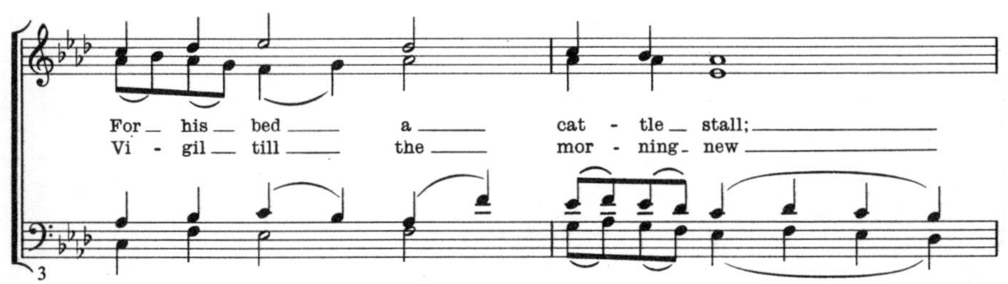

The dignity and beauty is lost if sung too quickly. Beat in crotchets (i.e. divided minims) but keep the flow and simplicity, with lightly-sung quavers. Ensure that excitement of the TB *Nowells* is felt in the climax of bars 13 and 14.

21

Joseph was an old man

(The Cherry Tree Carol)

Words
TRADITIONAL

Music arr. by
PETER WISHART
English tune

1

Joseph was an old man,
And an old man was he,
When he wedded Mary
In the land of Galilee.

2

Joseph and Mary walked
Through an orchard good,
Where was cherries and berries
So red as any blood.

3

Joseph and Mary walked
Through an orchard green,
Where was berries and cherries
As thick as might be seen.

4

O then bespoke Mary,
With words so meek and mild,
'Pluck me one cherry, Joseph,
For I am with child'.

5

O then bespoke Joseph,
With answer most unkind,
'Let him pluck thee a cherry
That brought thee now with child'.

6

O then bespoke the baby
Within his mother's womb—
'Bow down then the tallest tree
For my mother to have some'.

7

Then bowed down the highest tree,
Unto his mother's hand.
Then she cried, 'See, Joseph,
I have cherries at my command'.

8

O then bespake Joseph—
'I have done Mary wrong;
But now cheer up, my dearest,
And do not be cast down.

9

O eat your cherries, Mary,
O eat your cherries now,
O eat your cherries, Mary,
That grow upon the bough'.

10

Then Mary plucked a cherry,
As red as any blood;
Then Mary she went homewards
All with her heavy load.

There are several ways of performing this. Here are two suggestions for variety:

I (*Using all the verses*)
- 1 First version
- 2 First version
- 3 Second version
- 4 First version with soprano solo, ATB humming
- 5 First version with tenor solo, ATB humming
- 6 First version with soprano solo, unaccompanied
- 7 Second version
- 8 First version with tenor solo, ATB humming
- 9 First version
- 10 Second version

II (*Using six verses*)
- 1 First version
- 2 Second version
- 4 First version with soprano solo, ATB humming
- 7 Second version
- 9 First version
- 10 Second version

Let music flow, with no gap between verses. The metrical irregularity of the words needs very careful attention during rehearsal.

For the Elizabethan Singers

22

Let us securely enter

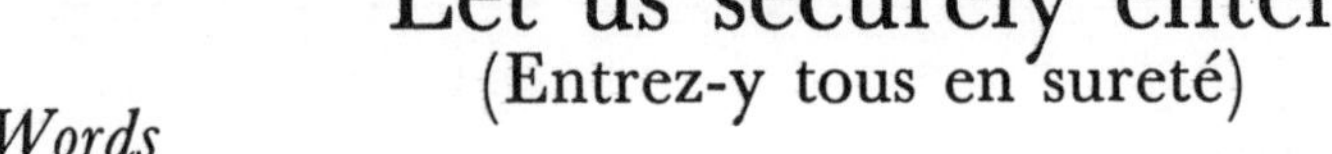

(Entrez-y tous en sureté)

Words
CHRISTIN PROST, 17th century
(*English translation by Edmund Rubbra*)

Music
EDMUND RUBBRA Opus 93
(*Tune written 1924: arr. SATB 1956*)

Andante moderato (♩ = 63)

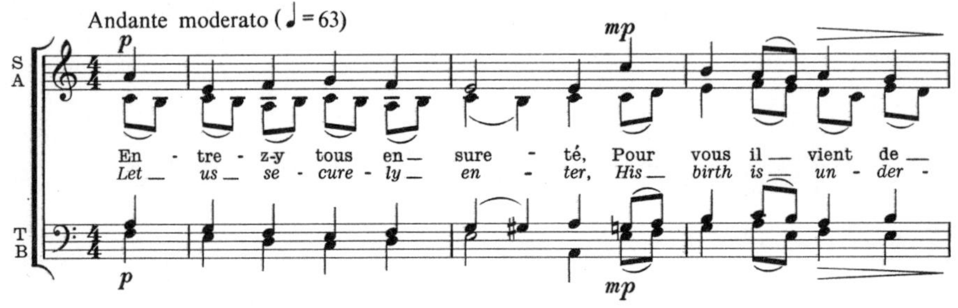

Reprinted by permission of Alfred Lengnick & Co. Ltd.

* If there are not sufficient tenors to give weight to this line, the music of the first verse should be repeated for six bars, then continue from bar 21.

Long, shapely phrases and quavers grouped in fours. Tender and expressive singing with no hurrying.

For R.N.F.

23

Lord Jesus once was a child

Words
RONALD DUNCAN*

Music
THOMAS EASTWOOD

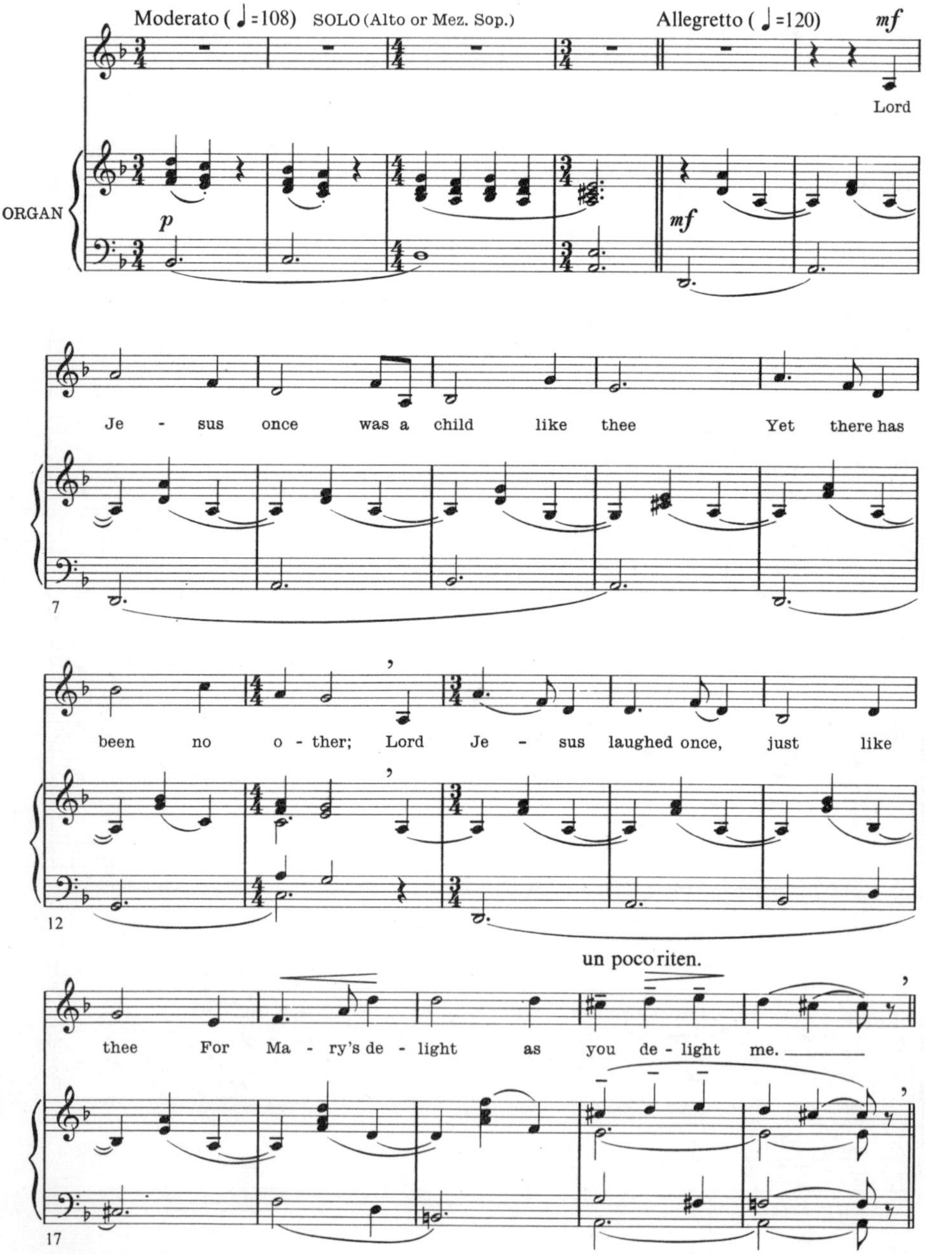
Moderato (♩=108)
SOLO (Alto or Mez. Sop.)
Allegretto (♩=120)
mf
ORGAN
p
mf
Lord Jesus once was a child like thee Yet there has been no other; Lord Jesus laughed once, just like thee For Mary's delight as you delight me.
un poco riten.
7
12
17

*By permission of Eric Glass Ltd., literary agent for Ronald Duncan

Moderato
un pochissimo meno
molto espress.
p
Weep, child, Weep for Je - sus' Mo - ther.
p
22
Allegretto
ALTO (Full)
mf
Lord Je - sus once had hair like thee,
mf
mp
26
mf SOPRANO (Full)
His could have been no sof - ter;
With skin as smooth and a mouth like
32
un poco riten.
And eyes that had wept be - fore they could see.
thee And eyes that had wept be - fore they could see.
un poco riten.
38

div. Moderato
un pochissimo meno
molto espress.
p
Weep, — child, — weep for Je - sus' Mo - ther. —
p
Moderato
p
43
Allegretto
f
Je - sus once had toys — like
f
Lord Je - sus once had toys like
Allegretto
f
felice
47
thee Throw, child, throw your ball high - er, And hands which his
mf
thee Throw, child, throw your ball high - er, And hands which his
mf
mf dolce
52

rall.
f
mo - ther kissed like me Hands that my hands
f
mo - ther kissed like me Hands that my hands
rall.
f

riten.
lunga
Molto moderato
p
nailed to a tree! Weep, child,
lunga
p
nailed to a tree! Weep, child,
riten.
lunga
Molto moderato

piu lento
ancora piu lento
pp
ppp molto distinto-come una voce
Weep, Weep for thy own mo-ther.
pp
ppp molto distinto-come una voce
Weep, Weep for thy own mo-ther.

This requires delicate and unhurried singing, with plenty of 'line'. The simplicity and charm must not lapse into mawkishness.

24

Lully, lulla, thou little tiny child

Words
15th CENTURY
(*from the Pageant of the Shearmen & Tailors, Coventry*)

Music
KENNETH LEIGHTON
Opus 25, No.2

Andante (cullante)

SOPRANO SOLO

p dolce

Lu - lly, lu - lla, thou lit-tle ti - ny child, By, by, lu - lly, lu - llay,

Andante (cullante)

S *pp* Lu - lly, lu - lla, lu - lly, lu - lla, lu - lly, lu - lla, lu - lly, lu - lla, lu - lly, lu - lla, lu - llay, lu - llay, *pp* Lu -

A *pp* Lu - lly, lu - lla, lu - lly, lu - lla, lu - lly, lu - lla, lu - lly, lu - lla, lu - lly, lu - lla, lu - llay, lu - llay, *pp* Lu -

T *pp* Lu - lly, lu - lla, lu - lly, lu - lla, lu - lly, lu - lla, lu - lly, lu - lla, lu - lly, lu - lla, lu - llay, lu - llay, *pp* Lu -

B *pp* Lu - lly, lu - lly, lu - lly, lu - lly, lu - lly, lu - lla, lu - llay, lu - llay, *pp* Lu -

Andante (cullante) (♩=108–16)

Accompt. (for rehearsal only)

pp *p dolce* *pp*

p
Lu - lly, thou lit-tle ti - ny child, Lu - lly, lu - lla, lu -
lly, lu - lla, lu - lly, lu - lla, lu - lly, lu - lla, lu -
lly, lu - lla, lu - lly, lu - lla, lu - lly, lu - lla, lu -
lly, lu - lla, lu - lly, lu - lla, lu - lly, lu - lla, lu -
lly, lu - lly, lu - lly, lu - lla, lu -
p
7
breve
un poco più mosso, più liberamente
llay.
breve
un poco più mosso, più liberamente
mf
llay. O sis - ters too, How may we do
breve
mf
llay, lu - llay. O sis - ters too, How may we do
breve
mf
llay. O sis - ters too, How may we do
breve
mf
llay. O sis - ters too, How may we do
breve
un poco più mosso, più liberamente
mf
10

cresc.
For to pre-serve this day? This poor young-ling For
For to pre-serve this day? This poor young-ling For
For to pre-serve this day? This poor young-ling For
For to pre-serve this day? This poor young-ling For
13
a tempo
SOPRANO SOLO
rall. pochiss.
mp
dim.
By, by, by, by, lu - lly, lu - llay,
rall. pochiss. a tempo
pp
whom we sing, By, by, by, by, lu -
whom we sing, By, by, by, by, lu -
whom we sing, By, by, by, by, lu -
whom we sing, By, by, by, by, lu -
rall. pochiss. a tempo
16

poco rall.
più mosso, agitato
lu - lly, lu - llay!
poco rall.
f più mosso, agitato
lly, lu - llay, lu - llay! He - rod, the king, In his
lly, lu - llay, lu - llay! He - rod, the king, In his
lly, lu - llay, lu - llay! He - rod, the king, In his
lly, lu - llay! He - rod, the king, In his
poco rall.
più mosso, agitato
19
ra - - - ging, Charg'd he hath this
ra - - - ging, Charg'd he hath this
ra - - - ging, Charg'd he hath this
ra - - - ging, Charg'd he hath this
22

day His men of might, In his own sight, All
day His men of might, In
day His men of might, In his own sight, In
day His men of might, In his own
25
rall.
chil - dren young to slay, to
his own sight, All chil - dren young to slay,
his own sight, All chil - dren young to slay,
sight, All chil - dren young to
rall.
28

Tempo I
SOPRANO SOLO p espress.
That woe - is me, woe is me, Poor child, - for
Tempo I
fz pp p pp
slay, to slay. That
slay, to slay. That
slay, to slay. That
slay, to slay. That
Tempo I
p espress.
fz pp p pp
31
thee! And ev - er mourn and
woe is me, Poor child, for thee! That woe is me, Poor
woe is me, Poor child, for thee! That woe is me, Poor
woe is me, Poor child, for thee! That woe is me, Poor
woe is me, That woe is me, Poor
35

Keep the opening chords soft so that the soloist can float the tone effortlessly. V. 3 needs clean rhythms and special care with consonants. Watch intonation in final chromatic chords.

To Kathleen Riddick

25

Nativity

Words
W. R. RODGERS*

Music
ELISABETH LUTYENS

* By permission of the author

SOPRANO (Solo or semichorus)
pp a tempo
And hark! the Herod-angels sing to-night!
pp
dolce
32
Man.
O-ver the Ma- - - - gi's tents their heart-less
37
song drones on through grum-bling glooms and weep - -
42
- - ing con - ti-nents.
p
High on his
p
46

farth - ing floor the air-man moons a - bove the mourn-ing
50
cresc.
town of Beth - le - hem; it is his foot - ling root and he — the
cresc.
54
(Solo)
f
flow'r, and he the flow'r and crown. O Cas-par,
f
60
Ped.
mp
Mel-chior, and Bal - tha - zar, come from your ca - ra - van and
66

rall.
tell me where you go and what new star you saw in Te - her -
p
72
BARITONE or ALTO(Solo)
più lento
quasi recit. ad lib.
p
an and what new man now hur-ries to be born out of our ad - dled
pp
78
earth, And O what sil-ly cor-ner of our-selves will see the low-ly
pp
81
birth.
(♩=72)
pp
84
Man.
(♩.=80)
pp poco a poco cresc.
91
Ped.

SOPRANO & TENOR (Full in octaves)
f
Strike, strike the gong of our song till
mf cresc.
94
souls take fire, clap hands and bel - low.
f
96
f
Dance, dance, leap high-er and lon-ger and hug each with your fel - low.
f
98
ff
Up with the win - dows, raise the shout.
ff
100

Hang all the Hal - le - lu - jahs out. Bring ev - 'ry stran-ger in, call for the lights and
102
fff
sing, sing, sing ____ for un - to you this day is born a
fff
104
King. ____
dim.
106
♩. = ♩
rall.
mp
pp
108

Originally for S solo and strings (or organ). The alternative suggestions are for choirs, although A and B can only comfortably take part as soloists in the recits. Treat vocal line expressively, with great care for intervals such as *E♮-A♭-D* (bars 35/6 and 43/4), *E♭-F♯* (bars 52/3 and 60/1), and the downward leaps in bars 65/7 and 70/1. Recits call for dramatic treatment. 12/8 section must be rhythmic and exciting.

26

Nowell, nowell, tidings true

(The Salutation Carol)

Words 15th CENTURY

Music arr. by RICHARD RODNEY BENNETT

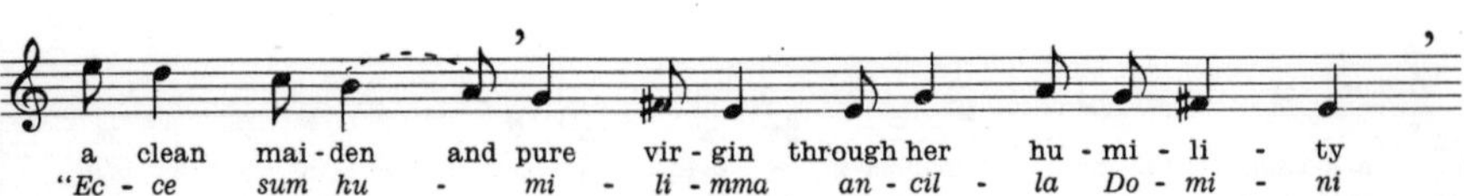

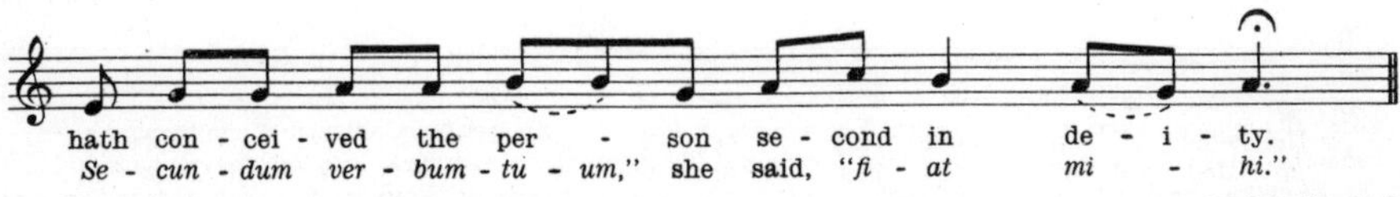

(to CODA after V. 7)

(back to v. 7, p. 98)

Vv. 3, 5
No - well, no - well, no -
No - well, no - well, no - well, this
No - well, no - well, no -
well, no - well.
is the sa - lu - ta - ti- of th'an - gel Ga - bri - el.
well, no - well.
TENOR
mf freely
3 Hail vir - gin ce - les - ti - al the meekest that ev - er was;
5 Then a - gain to her the an - gel cer - tain an - swer- éd;
Hail tem - ple of de - i - ty and mir - ror of all grace;
O La - dy dear be of good cheer, and dread thee ne'er a del;
Hail vir - gin pure, I thee en - sure, with - in full lit - tle space
Thou shalt con - ceive in thy bo - dy ve - ry God him - self
thou shalt re - ceive and him con - ceive that shall bring great so - lace.
in whose birth heav'n and earth shall joy, call - ed Em - man - u - el.
(back to v. 6, p. 99)
V. 4
No - well, No - well, No -
No - well, no - well, no - well, this

Take this quickly to represent the eagerness with which Gabriel brought his message. The solo section in each verse needs to be sung freely with suitable accentuation, and with adequate pause at the commas.

27

O leave your sheep

Words
FRENCH
(*English translation by Alice Raleigh*)

Music arr. by
KENNETH LEIGHTON
French tune

cresc.
mf
weep-ing in - to laugh - ter, O shep-herds seek your goal, Your Lord,
25
pp
your Lord, who co - meth to con - sole. Your
31
poco rall.
Lord, your Lord, who co - meth to con -
38
a tempo
sole.
mp
gaio
45

ALTO
mp ritmico
2 O leave your sheep, Your lambs that fol - low af - ter, O
BASS
mp ritmico
2 O leave your sheep, Your lambs that fol - low
p
51
leave the brook, The pas-ture and the crook, No lon - ger
af - ter, O leave the brook, The pas-ture and the crook. No
56
SOPRANO
mp
Turn weep-ing in - to laugh - ter, O shep-herds seek your goal,
ALTO
weep,
TENOR
mp
Turn weep-ing in - to laugh - ter, O
BASS
lon - ger weep,
61

mf
— Your Lord, who co - meth —
mp
Turn weep-ing in - to laugh - ter, O shep-herds seek your goal,
mf
shep-herds seek your goal, Your Lord, who
mf
your
66
to con - sole, Your Lord, who co - meth —
mf
— Your Lord, who co - meth — to con -
co - meth — to con - sole,
p
Lord, who co - meth — to con - sole.
71

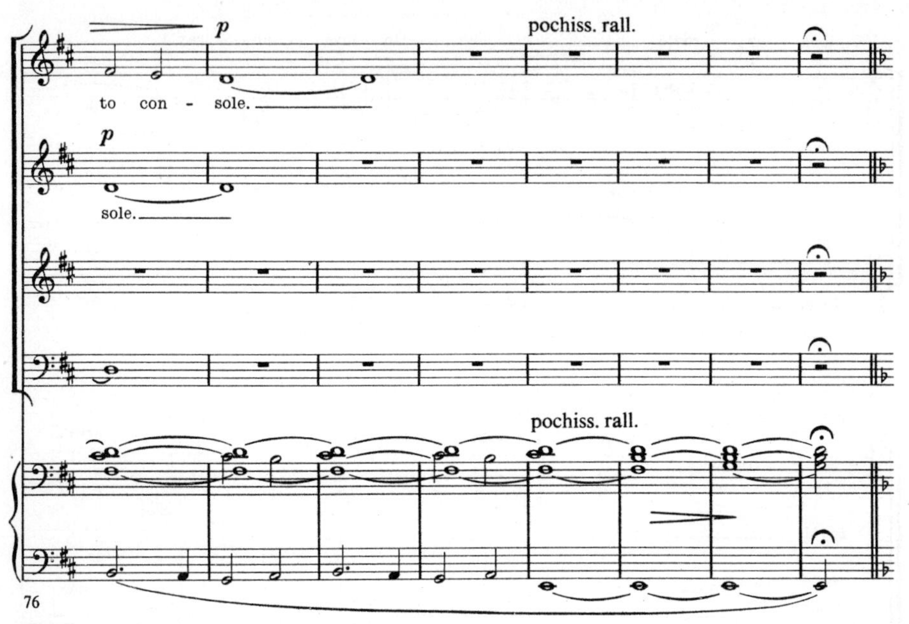

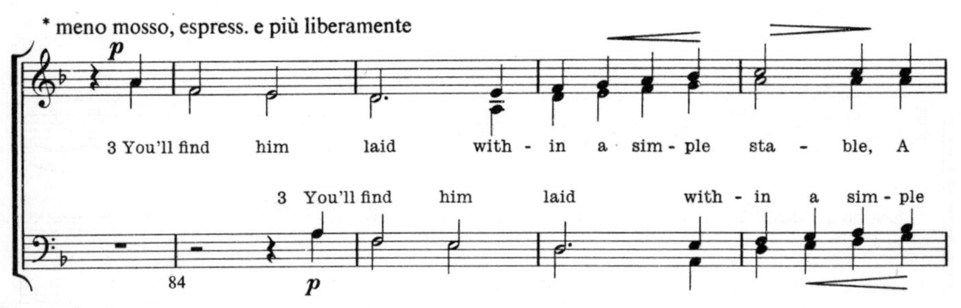

*Accompaniment ad lib.

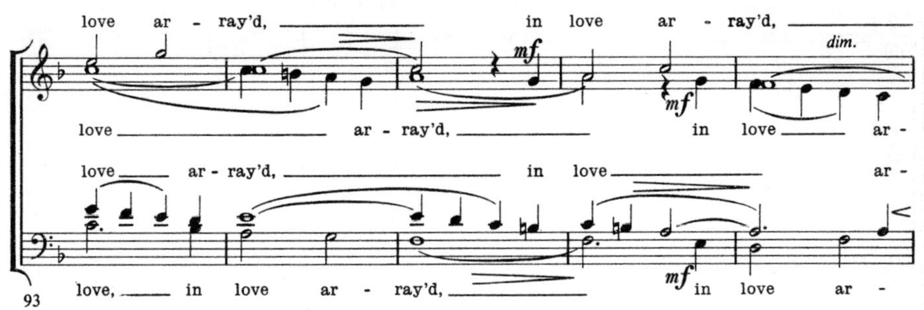
love ar - ray'd, in love ar - ray'd,
dim.
mf
love ar - ray'd, in love ar -
love ar - ray'd, in love ar -
mf
love, in love ar - ray'd, in love ar -
93

p
cresc.
ray'd, A love so deep, 'tis a - ble to
ray'd,
cresc.
p
ray'd, A love so deep, 'tis a - ble to
98

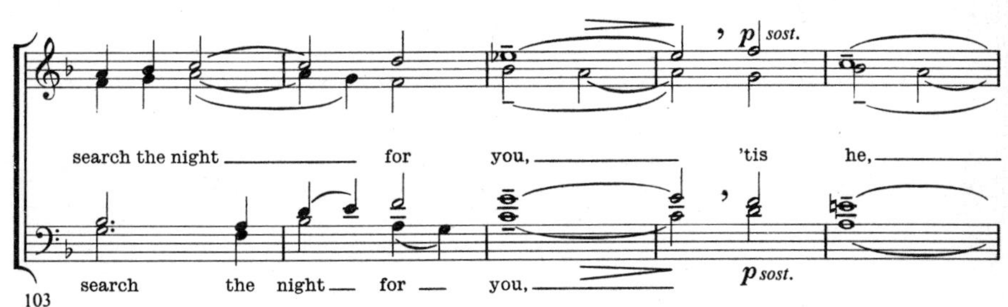
p sost.
search the night for you, 'tis he,
search the night for you,
p sost.
103

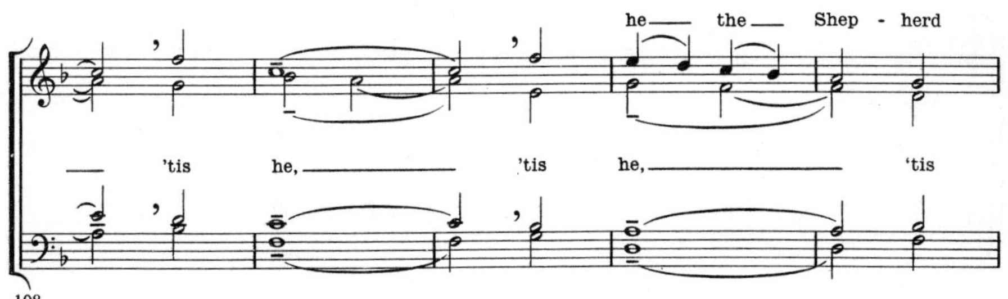
he the Shep - herd
'tis he, 'tis he, 'tis
108

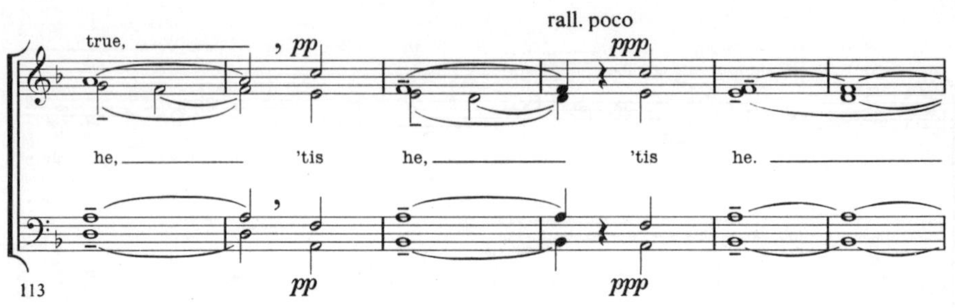
rall. poco
true,
pp
ppp
he, 'tis he, 'tis he.
pp
ppp
113

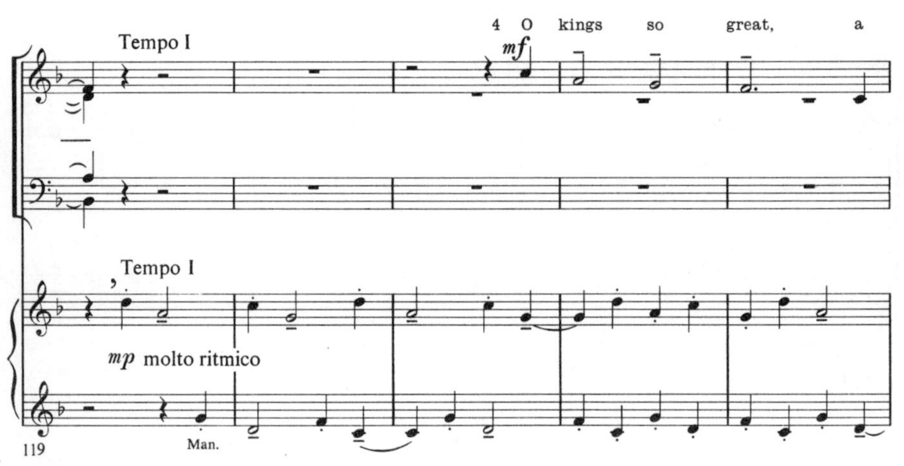
Tempo I
4 O kings so great, a
mf
Tempo I
mp molto ritmico
Man.
119

light is stream-ing o'er you, More ra - diant
f
mf
4 O kings so great, a
4 O kings so great, a light is stream-ing
mf
mf
4 More
cresc. poco a poco
124

far than di - a - dem or star,
light is stream-ing o'er you, More ra - diant far than di - a - dem or
o'er you, More ra - diant far than di - a - dem or star, Fore -
ra - diant far than di - a - dem or star, Fore -
129

declamato
ff
mf
star,
go, Fore - go your state, A ba - by lies be -
go, ff declamato
mf
ff
mf
134
Ped.

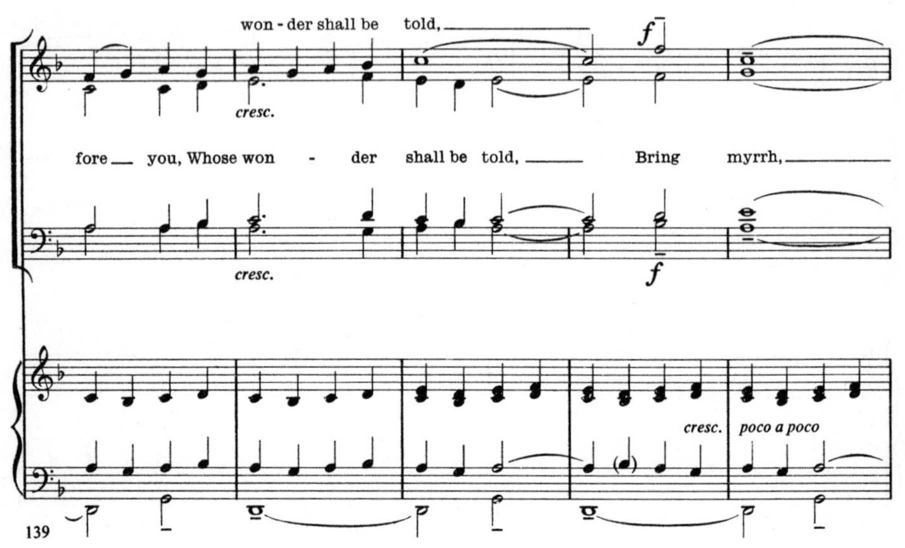
won - der shall be told,
f
cresc.
fore you, Whose won - der shall be told, Bring myrrh,
cresc.
f
cresc. poco a poco
139

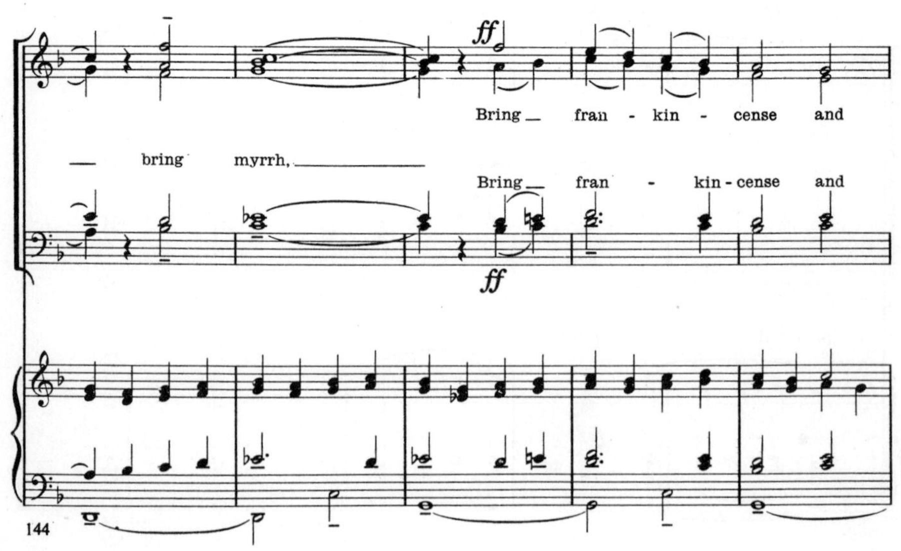
ff
Bring fran - kin - cense and
bring myrrh,
Bring fran - kin - cense and
ff
144

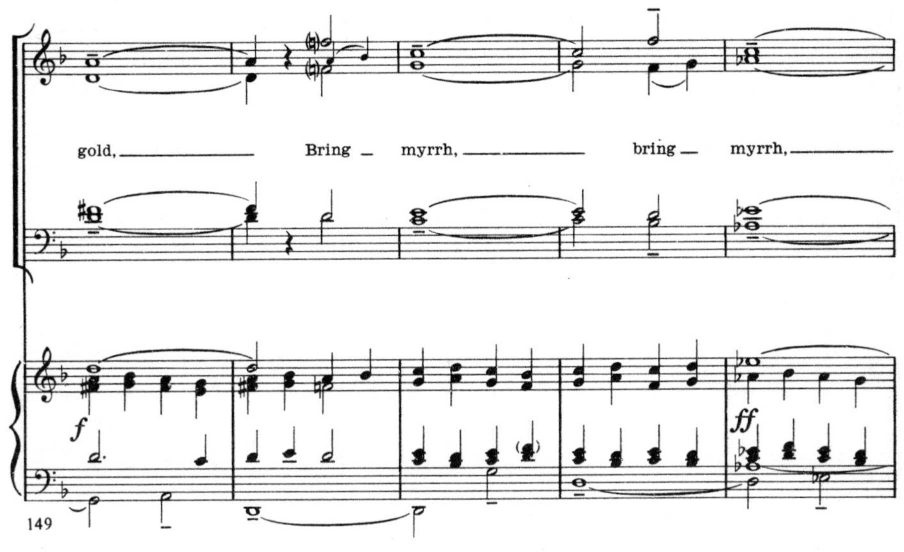

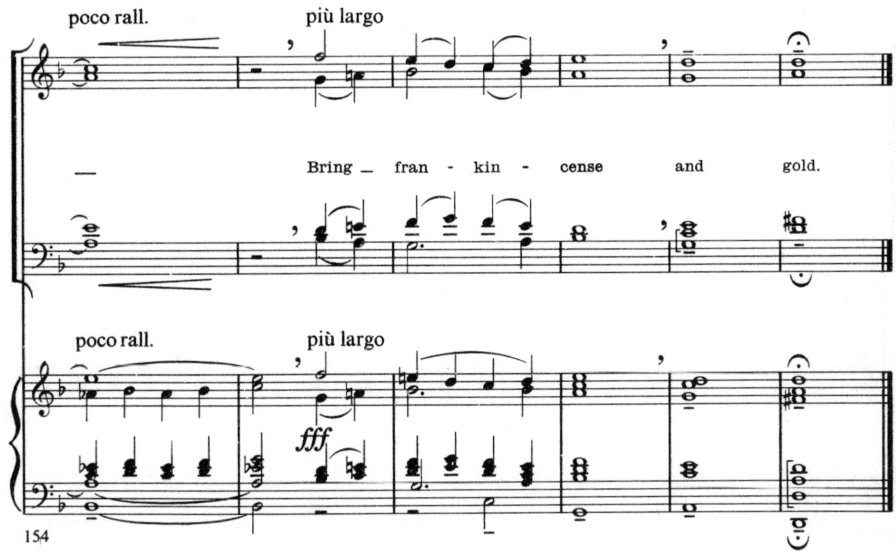

The first three verses need tender, expressive singing, with special care on high notes. V. 1 can be a solo. Ensure that the imitative leads of the final verse are clearly heard.

28

Our Lady's Song

Words
ANON, circa 1375

Music
NICHOLAS MAW
(*1961*)

4

mp dolciss.
For thi cradel is as a bere, Oxe
f
that me greveth sore;
mp dolciss.
For thi cradel is
mp dolciss.
For thi cradel is as a bere, Oxe
f
that me greveth sore;
mp dolciss.
For thi cradel is
8
mf
and asse beth thi fere:
p
Weepe
mf
as a bere, Oxe and asse beth thi fere:
p
Weepe ich mai
mf
and asse beth thi fere:
p
Weepe
mf
as a bere, Oxe and asse beth thi fere:
p
Weepe ich mai
11

poco
p
ich mai — thar - fore. Je-su, swete, beo noth wroth, Thou
thar - fore. Je-su, swete, —
Je-su, swete,
ich mai — thar - fore. Je-su, swete, beo noth wroth, Thou
Je-su, swete,
14
ich — nabbe clout — ne cloth
— beo noth — wroth, Thou ich — nabbe clout —
ich — nabbe clout — ne cloth
— beo noth — wroth, Thou ich — nabbe clout —
18

f
mp dolciss.
— The on for to — folde, — The — on to
f
— ne cloth — The on for to —
f
mp dolciss.
— The on for to — folde, — The — on to
f
— ne cloth — The on for to —
21
mf
folde ne — to — wrappe, For ich nabbe clout
mp dolciss.
mf
— folde, — The — on to folde ne — to — wrappe, For —
mf
folde ne — to — wrappe, For ich nabbe clout
mp dolciss.
mf
— folde, — The — on to folde ne — to — wrappe, For —
24

ST and AB must watch ensemble and intonation in octaves. Keep this exposed two-part writing very smooth and expressive, and do not hurry quavers. The progressions and off-beat rhythms in bars 10-12 need special care.

29

Out of your sleep arise

Words
14th CENTURY

Music
ANTHONY MILNER

kind now hath y - take All of a maid with-out a - ny
God man-kind now hath y - take All of a maid with-out a - ny
kind now hath y - take All of a maid with-out a - ny
God man-kind now hath y - take All of a maid with-out a - ny
10
make, Of all wo - men she bear-eth the bell.
make, Of all wo - men she bear-eth the bell.
make, Of all wo - men she bear-eth the bell.
make, Of all wo - men she bear-eth the bell.
13

mf
Glo - ry to God, glo - ry to God,
mf
Glo - ry to God, glo - ry to God,
17
mf
glo-ry to God in the high - - - est.
mf
glo-ry to God in the high - - - est.
glo-ry to God in the high - - est.
glo-ry to God in the high - - est.
20
24

SOPRANO
p
And through a mai - den fair and wise Now
ALTO p
And through a mai - den fair and wise Now man is made of
Ch.
p Gt.
30
Man.
mf
man is made of full great price; Now an - gels
mf
full great price; Now an - gels knee -
mf
34
knee - len to man's ser - vyse, And at this time
len to man's ser-vyse, And at this time
38
p
all this be - fell.
p
all this be - fell.
TENOR
p
Glo - ry to God, glo - ry to God,
p
41

p
glo-ry to God in the high - - - - est.
p
glo-ry to God in the high - - - - est.
p
glo-ry to God in the high - - est.
p
glo-ry to God in the high - - est.
Sw.
(Gt.)
45
BASS
mf
Now
mf
49
TENOR
mf
Now man is bright - er than the sun; Now man in
BASS
man is bright - er than the sun; Now man in hea-ven on high shall
53

heaven on high shall won;
Blessed be God this
won;
Blessed be God
this game
57
f
game is begun
And his mother that beareth the bell.
is begun
And his mother that beareth the bell.
mf
60
SOPRANO
Glory to God, glory to God,
glory to God in the
glory to God in the
64

mf
glo - ry to God in the high - - - est.
mf
glo - ry to God in the high - - - est.
high - - - - est.
high - - - - est.
Gt.
68
Ped.
mf
That e - ver was thrall, now is he free; That
mf
That e - ver was thrall, now is he free; That
mf
That e - ver was thrall, now is he free; That
mf
That e - ver was thrall, now is he free; That
71

f
e - ver was small, ___ now great ___ is she;
f
e - ver was small, ___ now great ___ is she;
f
e - ver was small, ___ now great ___ is she;
f
e - ver was small, ___ now great ___ is she;
f
75
mf
Now shall God deem both thee and me Un - to His bliss if we ___ do
mf
Now shall God deem both thee and me Un - to His bliss if we do
mf
Now shall God deem both thee and me Un - to His bliss if we do
mf
Now shall God deem both thee and me Un - to His bliss ___ if we do
mf
79

well.
glo-ry to God in the
well. Glo-ry to God, glo-ry to God, glo-ry to God in the
well. Glo-ry to God, glo-ry to God,
well.
82
high - - - est.
high - - - est.
glo-ry to God in the high - - est.
glo-ry to God in the high - - est.
cresc.
85

f
Now, bless - ed Bro-ther, grant us grace ____ At doom - es
f
Now, bless - ed Bro-ther, grant us grace ____ At
f
Now, bless - ed Bro-ther, grant us grace ____ At doom - es
f
Now, bless - ed Bro-ther, grant us grace ____ At
f
90
day ____ to see Thy face, ____ And in Thy court to have a
doom - es day to see Thy face, ____ And in Thy court to have a
day ____ to see Thy face, ____ And in Thy court to have a
doom - es day to see Thy face, ____ And in Thy court to have a
94

place That we may there sing
place That we may there sing
place That we may there sing
place That we may there sing
97
pochiss. rall.
a tempo
mf
Thee 'No - well.' Glo-ry to God, glo-ry to God,
Thee 'No - well.' Glo-ry to God, glo-ry to God,
Thee 'No - well.'
Thee 'No - well.'
100

mf
glo-ry to God in the
glo-ry to God in the high - -
glo-ry to God in the high - - -
glo-ry to God in the high - - - est, high -
104
ff
f
high - - - - - - - - -
- - - est, glo-ry to God in the high - -
est, high - - - - - -
- - - est, glo-ry to God in the high - -
108

Not only must the rhythms dance, but the words need crisp singing and enunciation, even in the softer sections. A strict adherence to the expression marks is important.

30

Remember, O thou man

Words
THOMAS RAVENSCROFT
(*from his* Melismata *1611*)

Music
ARTHUR OLDHAM

TENOR SOLO
pent. 2 Re - mem-ber God's good-ness, Re - mem-ber God's
pent.
O thou man, O thou man,
12
good - ness, And pro - mise made: Re - mem - ber God's good - ness,
And pro - mise made: How his on -
17
thou man, thou man, Be not a - fraid.
- ly Son he sent, Our sins for to re - dress: Be not a - fraid.
21
Allegro con spirito (♪ = 144)
3 The an - gels all did sing, O thou man, O thou man, The
25
The an - gels did sing, O thou man, O thou man, The

The
an-gels all did sing, On Si-on hill: The an-gels all did
29
an - gels did sing, On Si-on hill: The an - gels did

psub.
sing, Praise t'our heav'n-ly King, And peace to man li-ving, And
34
sing, Praise to our King, And peace to man li-ving, And
psub.

peace to man li-ving, The angels all did sing, With right good - will.
39
peace to man li-ving, The an- gels did sing, With right good - will.

Andante (Tempo I)
SOPRANO SOLO
mf
4 To Beth-lem did they go, To Beth-lem did they
p
O thou man, O thou man,
45
p

go This thing to see: To Beth-lem did they go, thou
This thing to see: To see whe - ther it was so,
49
man, thou man, To set us free.
TENOR SOLO
5 In Beth- lem was he
Whe-ther Christ was born or no To set us free.
54
born, In Bethlem was he born, For man-kind dear: In
O thou man, O thou man, For man-kind dear:
58
Beth-lem was he born, thou man, thou
For us that were for - lorn, And there - fore took no
63

SOP. & TENOR SOLI
man, Our sins to bear. 6 Give thanks to God al - ways, Give
scorn Our sins to bear. Give thanks to God al-ways, O thou man, O thou man, Give
67
thanks to God al-ways With hearts most jol - ly: Give thanks to God
thanks to God al - ways, With hearts most jol - ly: Give thanks to God
72
al - ways, thou man, thou man, Ho - ly, Ho - ly.
always Up-on this bles - sed day; Let all men sing and say: Ho - ly, Ho- ly.
76
Allegro con spirito
The an - gels all did sing, O thou man, O thou man, The
81
The an - gels did sing, O thou man, O thou man, The

The *Andante* solos need expressive rubato and the chorus chords a contrasting precision. Rhythmic gaiety must be keenly felt in the fast sections.

31

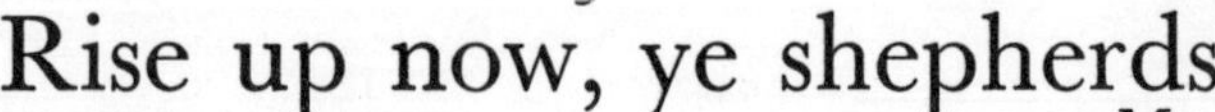

Rise up now, ye shepherds

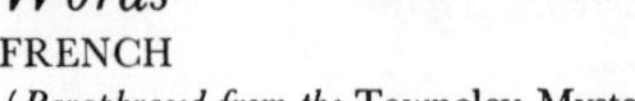

Words
FRENCH
(*Paraphrased from the* Towneley Mysteries)

Music arr. by
ALAN BUSH
French tune

Allegro vivace (♩ = 108)

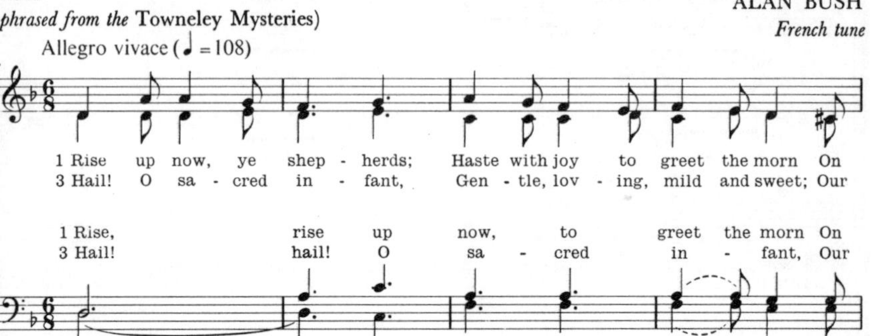

REFRAIN

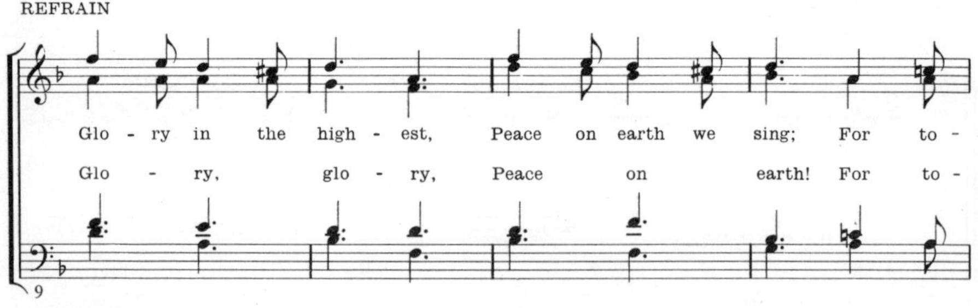

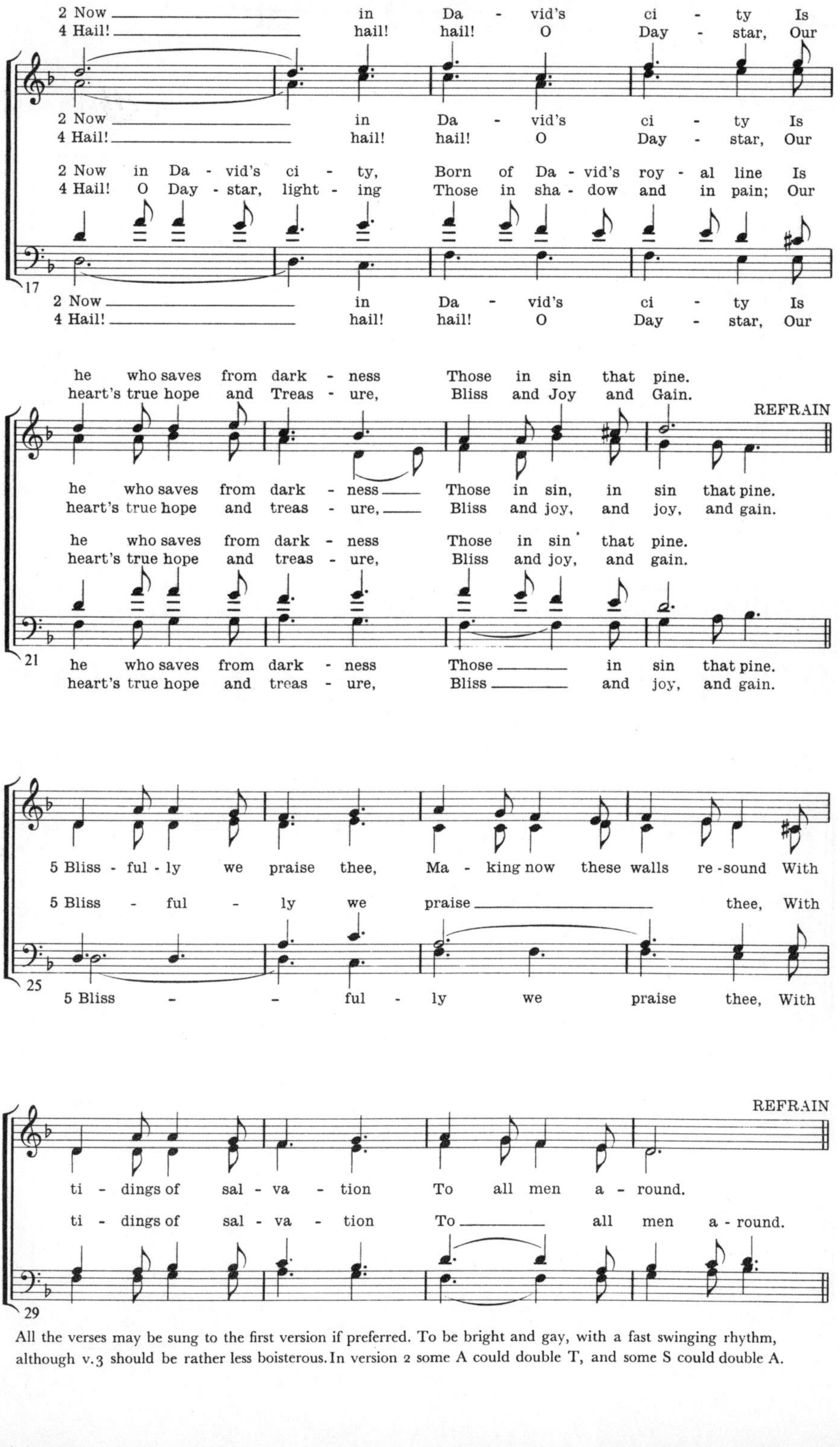

2 Now ___ in Da - vid's ci - ty Is
4 Hail! ___ hail! hail! O Day - star, Our

2 Now ___ in Da - vid's ci - ty Is
4 Hail! ___ hail! hail! O Day - star, Our

2 Now in Da - vid's ci - ty, Born of Da - vid's roy - al line Is
4 Hail! O Day - star, light - ing Those in sha - dow and in pain; Our

17

2 Now ___ in Da - vid's ci - ty Is
4 Hail! ___ hail! hail! O Day - star, Our

he who saves from dark - ness Those in sin that pine.
heart's true hope and Treas - ure, Bliss and Joy and Gain.

REFRAIN

he who saves from dark - ness ___ Those in sin, in sin that pine.
heart's true hope and treas - ure, ___ Bliss and joy, and joy, and gain.

he who saves from dark - ness Those in sin that pine.
heart's true hope and treas - ure, Bliss and joy, and gain.

21

he who saves from dark - ness Those ___ in sin that pine.
heart's true hope and treas - ure, Bliss ___ and joy, and gain.

All the verses may be sung to the first version if preferred. To be bright and gay, with a fast swinging rhythm, although v. 3 should be rather less boisterous. In version 2 some A could double T, and some S could double A.

32

Shepherds, come

mp
Prin - ces, come, mon-archs, come From the ci - ties where your care is
mp
Prin - ces, come, mon-archs, come From the ci - ties where care is
mp
Prin - ces, come, mon-archs, come From the ci - ties' care a -
mp
hem! Prin - ces, come, mon-archs, come From the ci - ties a -
mp
7
sleep - ing.
mp
See the child,
sleep - ing.
mp
See the child,
sleep - ing.
mp
See the
mf
sleep - ing. Brothers, come a - way to Beth - le - hem!
mp
See the
mp
mf
11

rall.
Grave and mild, Laid in a man-ger with Ma-ry his mo-ther.
Grave and mild, Laid in a man-ger with Ma-ry his mo-ther.
rall.
child, Grave and mild, in a man - ger with his mo-ther. O
child, Grave and mild, in man - ger with his mo-ther.
rall.
14
a tempo
mp
Shepherds, come, prin-ces, come To the light of him and of his ris - ing.
mp
Shepherds, come, prin-ces, come To the light of him and his ris - ing.
a tempo
mp
come, shepherds, come, prin-ces, come To his light and to his ris - ing.
mp
Come, shepherds, come, prin-ces, come To his light, his ris - ing,
a tempo
mp
19

un poco più mosso
mf
Bro thers, come a - way.
mf un poco più mosso
Shepherd on the hill, what glo - ry is
mf
ris - ing.
Shepherd on the hill, what glo - ry is
mf
un poco più mosso
mf
24
mf
Glo - ry, glo - ri - a!
Glo - ry, glo - ri -
mf
Glo - ry, glo - ri - a!
Glo - ry, glo - ri -
this?
Seraphim and an-gels sing in re - joic - ing,
this?
Seraphim and an-gels sing in re - joic - ing,
28

dim.

a! Come, come,

dim.

a! Come, come,

dim.

O - ver - head a great star beck - ons and calls to all men,

dim.

O - ver - head a great star beck - ons and calls to all men,

dim.

31

a tempo

rall. mp

come, come, Prais-ing God, prais - ing God

mp

come, come, Prais-ing God, prais - ing God

a tempo

rall. mp

all men, all men, come, Prais - ing God, prais-ing God

mp

all men, all men, come praise, Prais-ing God, prais-ing God

rall. a tempo

mp

34

Reflects eagerness of the shepherds, and the sense of awe at the sight of the angels. Music must flow, becoming slightly more detached in the 7/8 bars.

33

Shepherds! shake off your drowsy sleep

Words
FRENCH
(*English translation anon*)

Music arr. by
BERNARD NAYLOR
Besançon tune

Allegro moderato (♩. =80)

Passages marked ⌈ ⌉ may be sung by solo or semichorus

2

Hark! even now the bells ring round,
Listen to their merry sound;
Hark! how the birds new songs are making
As if winter's chains were breaking.
Shepherds! the chorus come and swell!
Sing Noel, oh sing Noel!

3

See how the flowers all burst anew
Thinking snow is summer dew;
See how the stars afresh are glowing,
All their brightest beams bestowing.
Shepherds! the chorus come and swell!
Sing Noel, oh sing Noel!

4

Cometh at length the age of peace,
Strife and sorrow now shall cease;
Prophets foretold the wondrous story
Of this Heaven-born Prince of Glory.
Shepherds! the chorus come and swell!
Sing Noel, oh sing Noel!

5

Shepherds! then up and quick away,
Seek the Babe ere break of day;
He is the hope of every nation,
All in Him shall find salvation.
Shepherds! the chorus come and swell!
Sing Noel, oh sing Noel!

A gossamer-like texture that needs delicate singing. Rehearse S and T so that they pass the tune to and fro without hesitation. Always keep the gentle swing of the tune uppermost in mind.

34

Silent night

Words
W. G. ROTHERY

Music arr. by
ALAN RIDOUT
Tune by Franz Grüber

Cloying sentimentality will be avoided if this is sung clearly and expressively at the speed indicated. Beat six quavers in the bar—and remember the underlying lilt of two-in-the-bar. S must observe opening dynamics exactly.

35

Sweet was the song

Words
WILLIAM BALLET
(*from his Lute Book, 17th century*)

Music
JOHN ROSE

Moderate pace (♩=c.104)

S A / T B

mp

Sweet was the song the Vir - gin sang, When she to Beth - lem

mp

4 Ju - da came And was de - li - vered of __ a son, That

Echo

'Lul - la, lul - la, lul -

mf *p*

7 bles - sed Je - sus hath __ to name: lul - la,

mf

la, lul - la, lul - la,

mf *mp*

10 lul - la, lul - la, lul - la - by.' 'Sweet

p *mf* *mp*

poco cresc.

13 babe,' sang she, 'My son, And eke a __ Sa - viour

poco cresc.

To be sung simply and delicately, with careful accentuation. Let the quavers flow.

36

Tell us, thou clear and heavenly tongue

(The Star-Song)

Words
ROBERT HERRICK

Music
ADRIAN CRUFT Opus 42

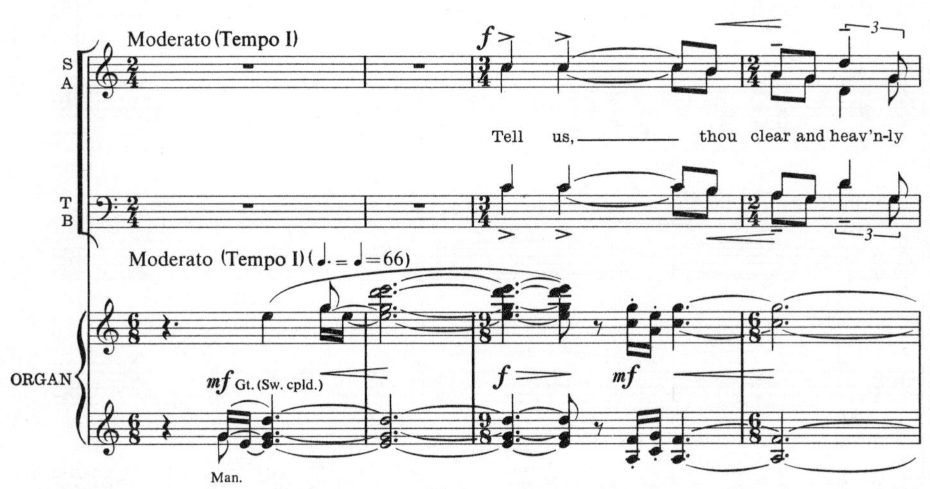

f
(9) mf
rall.
sprung? Lies He the Li - ly - banks a -
mf
poco f
9
meno mosso (Tempo II)
mp
pp
mong? Or
meno mosso (Tempo II)(♩. = ♩ = 56)
p (Sw.)
12
Ped. 16', 8'
Tempo I
say, if this new Birth of ours
Tempo I
pp
15

Tempo II
sleeps,
laid with - in some Ark of
Sleeps,
sleeps,
sleeps,
laid,
Tempo II
18
Flow'rs,
Flow'rs,
Sleeps,
Sleeps,
Spangled with dew - light;
laid with-in some Ark of
Flow'rs,
21
Tempo I
thou canst clear
All
doubts,
and
Tempo I
24
Man.

ma-ni-fest the where. De - clare to us, bright
27
if we shall seek Him
Star, if we shall seek Him
if we shall seek Him in the Morn-ing's
if we shall seek Him
30
Or search the beds of spi - ces through,
blush - ing cheek,
Or
33

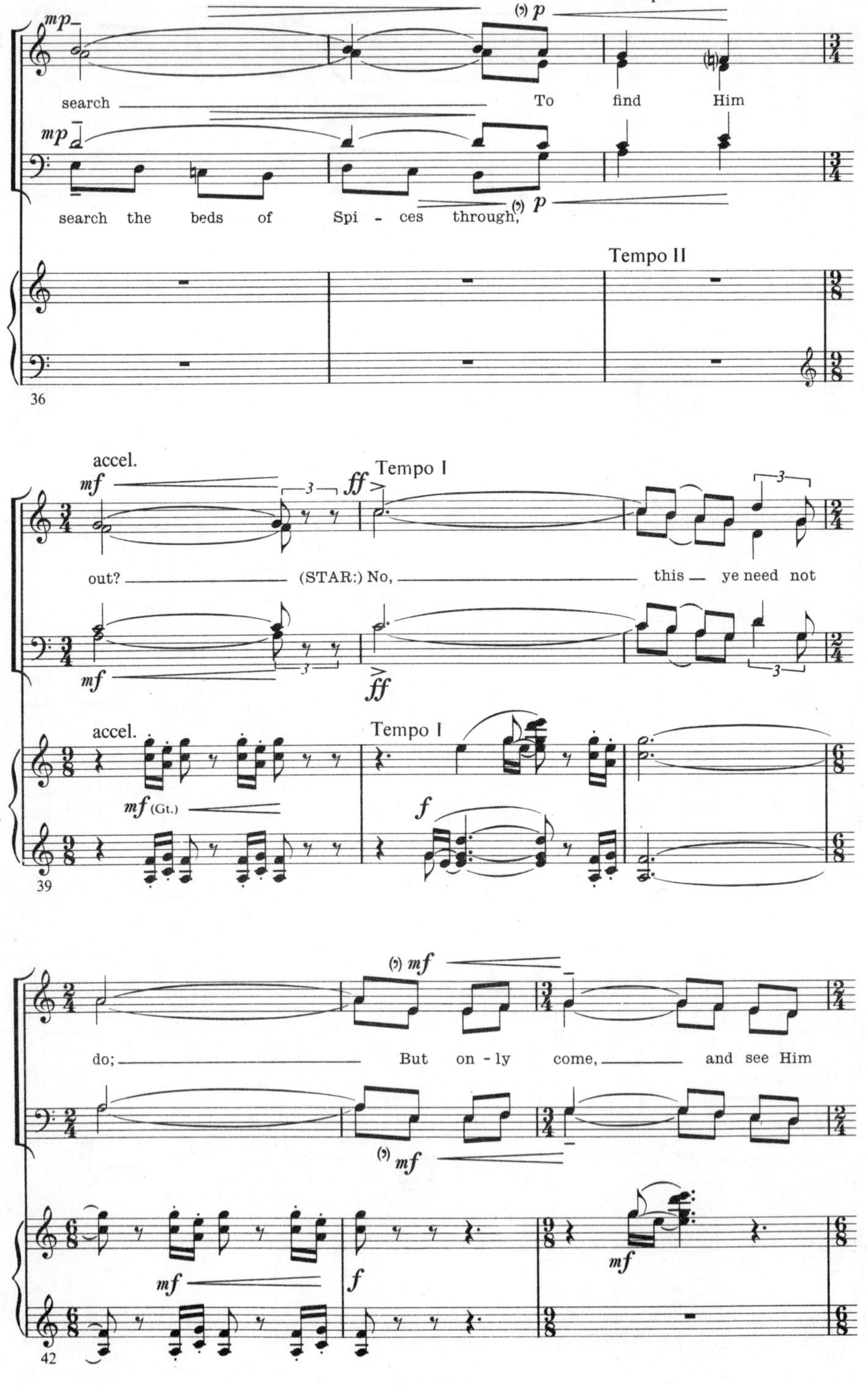
Tempo II
search
To find Him
search the beds of Spi - ces through,
Tempo II
36
accel.
Tempo I
out?
(STAR:) No,
this ye need not
accel.
Tempo I
(Gt.)
39
do;
But on - ly come,
and see Him
42

This needs sensitivity, with special care for rhythm, particularly in the main accompanying figure (differentiate between the staccato and phrased semi-quavers). ATB lose the final 'k' of 'cheek' in bar 35. The tempo changes need careful judgement.

37

The Coventry Carol

Words
15th CENTURY
(*from the Pageant of the Shearmen & Tailors, Coventry*)

Music arr. by
JOHN ROSE
English tune

For to pre - serve this day This poor young - ling For
18
whom we do sing, (Full) By by, lul - ly, lul - lay.
poco rall.
p
By by, By by,
p
By by, lul - ly, lul - lay.
poco rall.
mf Diaps.
23
TENOR &BASS (FULL)
mf
in his ra -
He - rod, the king, in his ra -
28
ging, Char - ged he hath this
- ging, Char - ged he hath this day His
32

of own
men of might In his own sight, All young chil -
36
Ped.
SOPRANO SOLO
molto espress.
f
mf
That woe is me, that
più p
That woe is
dren to slay.
pp
più p
dim.
pp
41
woe is me, Poor child for thee!
And e - ver
me, Poor child for thee! And e - ver
And e - ver
44

Treat expressively, with a neat rhythmic flow between voices and organ in vv. 2 and 3. Interpret in as dramatic a manner as the text demands. The S solo in the last verse may be taken by a few voices.

38

The First Christmas

Words
ANON*

Music
PETER RACINE FRICKER
(*1938*)

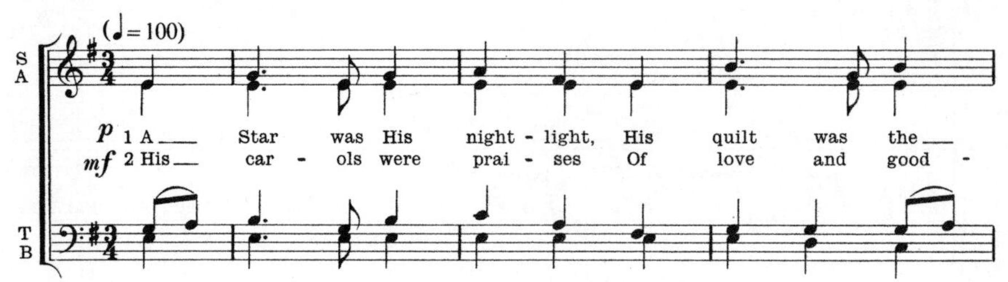

*The publishers regret that they have been unable to trace the author

Tender and simple. Four-bar phrases, of which the third provides the climax both times.

39

The first Nowell

Words
TRADITIONAL

Music arr. by
JOHN GARDNER
English tune

keep - ing their sheep, In a cold win - ter's night that
stop and stay Right o - ver the place where
his pre - sence Both gold and myrrh and
15
was so deep:
Je - sus lay:
frank - in - cense:
No - well, No - well, No - well, No -
19
well, Born is the King of Is - ra - el!
24
Accompt. ad lib.
2 They look - ed up and saw a star, Shin -
S
A
p
2 They look - ed up and saw a star, Shin - ing
2 They look - ed up and saw a star, Shin - ing
T
B
p
29
2 They look - ed up and saw a star, Shin - ing

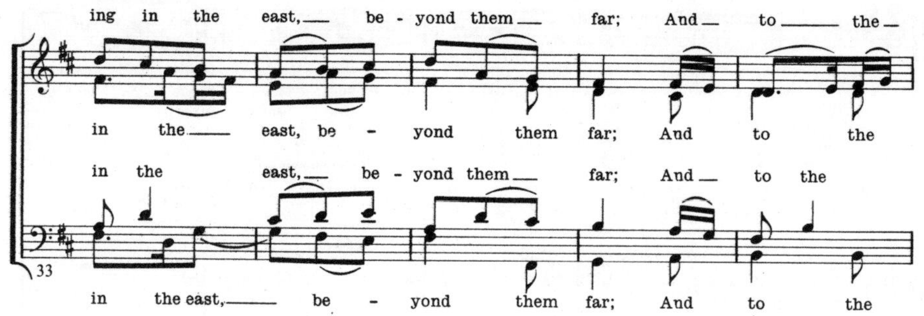
ing in the east, be - yond them far; And to the
in the east, be - yond them far; And to the
in the east, be - yond them far; And to the
33
in the east, be - yond them far; And to the

earth it gave great light, And so it con - tin - ued both
earth it gave great light, And so it con - tin - ued both
earth it gave great light, And so it con -
38
earth it gave great light, And so it con -

day and night: No - well, No - well, No - well, No -
day and night: No - well, No - well, No -
tin - ued both day and night: No - well, No - well, No -
43
tin - ued both day and night: No - well, No - well, No -

well, Born is the King of Is - ra - el!
well, Born is the King of Is - ra - el!
well, Born is the King of Is - ra - el!
48
well, Born is the King!

SOPRANO(Descant)
f
3 And by the light of that same star,
8 Then let us all with one ac-cord
f Unison (A T B)
3 And by the light of that same star, Three
8 Then let us all with one ac - cord Sing
f
Ped.
53
Three Wise Men came from country far To seek
Sing prai-ses to our heav'n-ly Lord, That hath
Wise Men came from coun - try far To seek for a
prai - ses to our heav'n - ly Lord, That hath made
57
for a king was their in-tent And to fol - low the star
made heav'n and earth of naught, And with his blood man-
king was their in - tent And to fol-low the star where-so-
heav'n and earth of naught, And with his blood man-
62

— where-so - - ev - er it went:
- kind hath — bought: —
No - well, — No - well, No -
ev - er it went:
kind — hath bought:
No - well, — No - well, No - well, No -
67
well, — Born — is the — King! —
well, Born is the King — of Is - ra - el!
72
D 𝄋 (for verse 4)
UNACCOMPANIED
p espress.
S
5 Then did — they know as - sur - ed - ly With - in that —
A
p espress.
5 (No - well, — No - well, — No - well, — No -
T
p espress.
5 Then did — they know — as - sur - ed - ly — With -
B
p espress.
77
5 (No - well, — No -

house_ the King_ did lie:
well,___ No - well.)___ (No - well,___ No -
in_that house___ the King_did lie:_ One_ en - tered in_then for to
82
well, No - well.)___ One en - tered in then for_ to
No - well,_ No - well, No - well.___ No - well,_ No -
well, No - well, No-well, No-well, No - well, No - well.) No -
see,_ And found the babe in___ po - ver - ty:
88
see, And found_ the babe_ in po - ver - ty:
cresc.
f
p
well, No - well, No - well, Born is the King_ of Is - ra - el!
well,_ No - well, No - well, Born_ is_ the King_ of_ Is - ra - el!
mf
Born_ is_the_ King_ of_ Is - ra - el!
94
No - well,_ No - well, No - well, Born_ is_ the King!___

D.𝄋 *(for verse 6)*

SOPRANO(Solo ad lib.)
p espressivo
7 Be - tween an ox - stall and an ass This
child tru - ly there born he was; For want of
cloth - ing they did him lay All in the man - ger a -
mong the hay: No - well, No - well, No - well, No -
well, Born is the King of Is - ra - el!
p sempre legato
Man.
Ped. 8′
ppp
Man.

Bramley's 1871 version omits vv. 2, 5, 7 and 9; they are rarely sung today. They appear here in elaborate versions for those who would meet their challenge, leaving vv. 1, 3, 4, 6 and 8 for unison voices and optional descant. A brisk speed (one-in-the-bar) is essential.

For June Gordon & the Haddo House Choral Society, 1957

40 The Holly and the Ivy

Words TRADITIONAL

Music arr. by BENJAMIN BRITTEN

English tune

ALTO(MEZ. SOP.) SOLO
mf or SEMICHORUS

3 The hol - ly bears a co - lour As green as a - ny tree; And

TENOR (Full)
pp

3 It bears co - lour, green as a tree,

REFRAIN

Ma - ry bore sweet Je - sus Christ To set poor sin - ners free.

Je - sus Christ set sin-ners free.

SOPRANO (Full)
p
ten.
Je -

ALTO(Full)
ten.

4 A ber - ry, red as blood, Ma -

BASS(BARITONE) SOLO or SEMICHORUS
f

4 The hol-ly bears a ber - ry As red as a - ny blood, And

- sus Christ to do good.
REFRAIN

- ry bore to do sin-ners good.

Ma - ry bore sweet Je-sus Christ To do poor sin - ners good.

ALTO(MEZ. SOP.) SOLO
mf or SEMICHORUS

5 The hol - ly bears a pri - ckle As sharp as a - ny thorn; And

TENOR (Full)
pp

5 It bears pri - ckle sharp as a thorn;

REFRAIN

Ma - ry bore sweet Je - sus Christ At Christ-mas day in the morn.

Je - sus Christ at Christ - mas morn.

TENOR SOLO *p* or SEMICHORUS

6 The holy bears a bark As bitter as any gall, And Mary bore sweet Jesus Christ For to redeem us all.

BASS (Full) *pp*

6 A bark bitter as gall, 49 — Mary bore to redeem us all. 53

REFRAIN

SOPRANO SOLO *pp* or SEMICHORUS

7 The holly and the ivy Are trees that's both well known; Of all the trees that grows in woods, The holly bears the crown.

ALTO (Full) *ppp*

7 The holly well known; 57 — the holly bears crown. 61

REFRAIN

S A *f*

The rising of the sun, The running of the deer, The playing of the merry harp, Sweet singing in the choir.

T B *f* 65 69

Sing the verses at a more relaxed tempo than the refrain. Ensure that the refrain is taken up quickly each time; a short break before verses seems appropriate. The solos may be sung by chorus or semichorus.

41

The Infant King

Words
S. BARING-GOULD*

Music arr. by
DESMOND RATCLIFFE
Basque tune

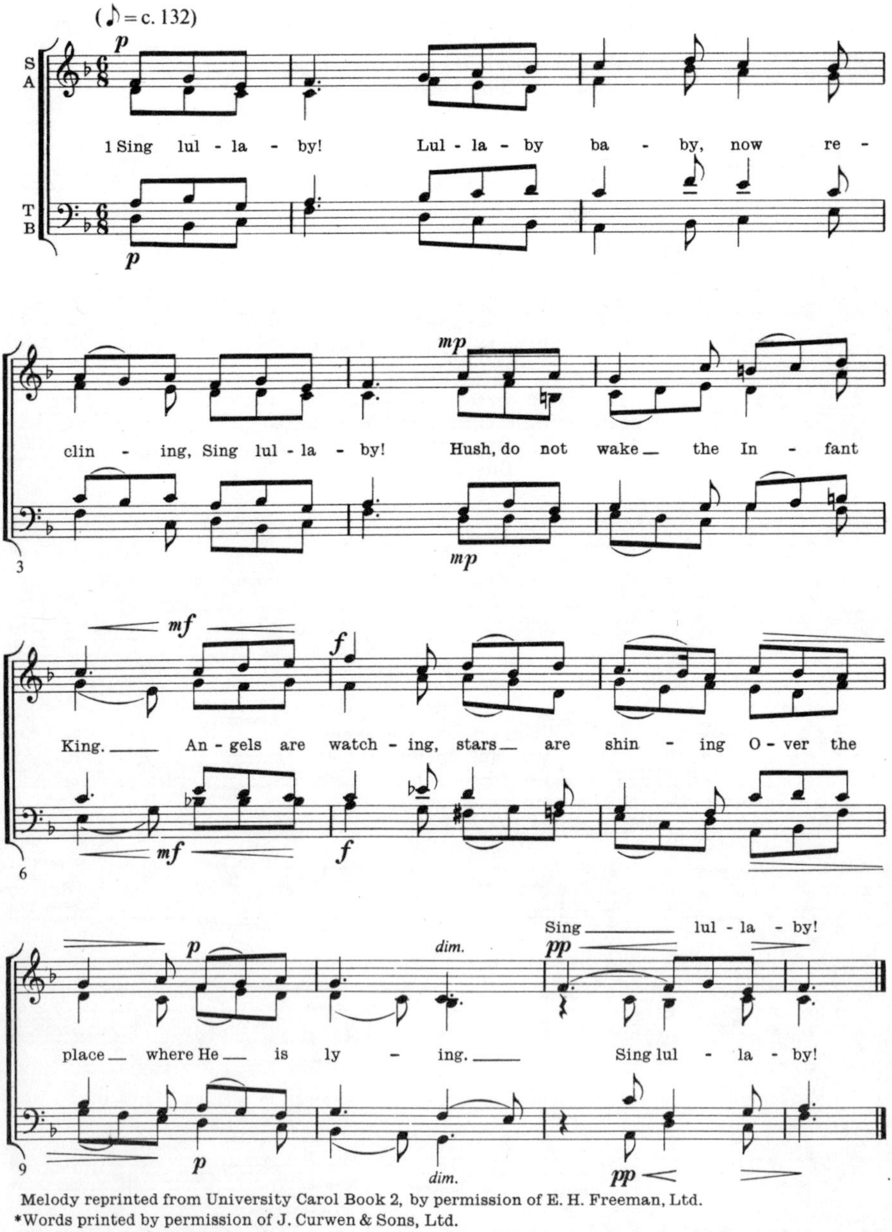
(♪ = c. 132)
S A
T B
1 Sing lul - la - by! Lul - la - by ba - by, now re -
clin - ing, Sing lul - la - by! Hush, do not wake the In - fant
King. An - gels are watch - ing, stars are shin - ing O - ver the
place where He is ly - ing.
Sing lul - la - by!
Sing lul - la - by!
dim.
3
6
9

Melody reprinted from University Carol Book 2, by permission of E. H. Freeman, Ltd.
*Words printed by permission of J. Curwen & Sons, Ltd.
Beat in quavers but remember the expressive lilt of a lullaby. Aim for unanimity in the chording, and restrain the S from haste in the penultimate bar.

2

Sing lullaby!
Lullaby baby, now a-sleeping,
Sing lullaby!
Hush, do not wake the Infant King.
Soon will come sorrow with the morning,
Soon will come bitter grief and weeping:
Sing lullaby!

3

Sing lullaby!
Lullaby baby, now a-dozing,
Sing lullaby!
Hush, do not wake the Infant King.
Soon comes the cross, the nails, the piercing,
Then in the grave at last reposing:
Sing lullaby!

4

Sing lullaby!
Lullaby! is the babe a-waking?
Sing lullaby!
Hush, do not stir the Infant King.
Dreaming of Easter, gladsome morning.
Conquering Death, its bondage breaking:
Sing lullaby!

42

Words
GERMAN
(*English translation by Joy Finzi*)*

The Linden Tree

Music arr. by
JEREMY DALE ROBERTS
German tune

*Words Publisher's Copyright

*Altos and Basses hum higher octave if possible

sfp ten. dim. pp ppp

sfp ten. dim. pp ppp

ten. dim. p

72 Ho - ly Ghost, so all may see, shall cast his sha - dow o'er thee.

SOLO I or SEMICHORUS

più mosso (♩.=69)

f jubilante

A joy doth quick-en in my heart; Ac - cor - ding to thy

SII SOLO or SEMICHORUS

f jubilante

80 'A joy doth quick-en

SI Full *f*

tell - ing, A won - drous star shall stand a - part, A

SII Full *f*

in my heart; A won - drous star shall

AI *f*

87 A won - drous

won - drous star shall stand a - part, A won - drous star shall stand a -

stand a - part, A won - drous star shall stand a - part, A won - drous

star shall stand a - part, A won - drous star shall stand a - part, A

AII *f*

93 A won - drous star shall stand a - part, A won - drous star shall

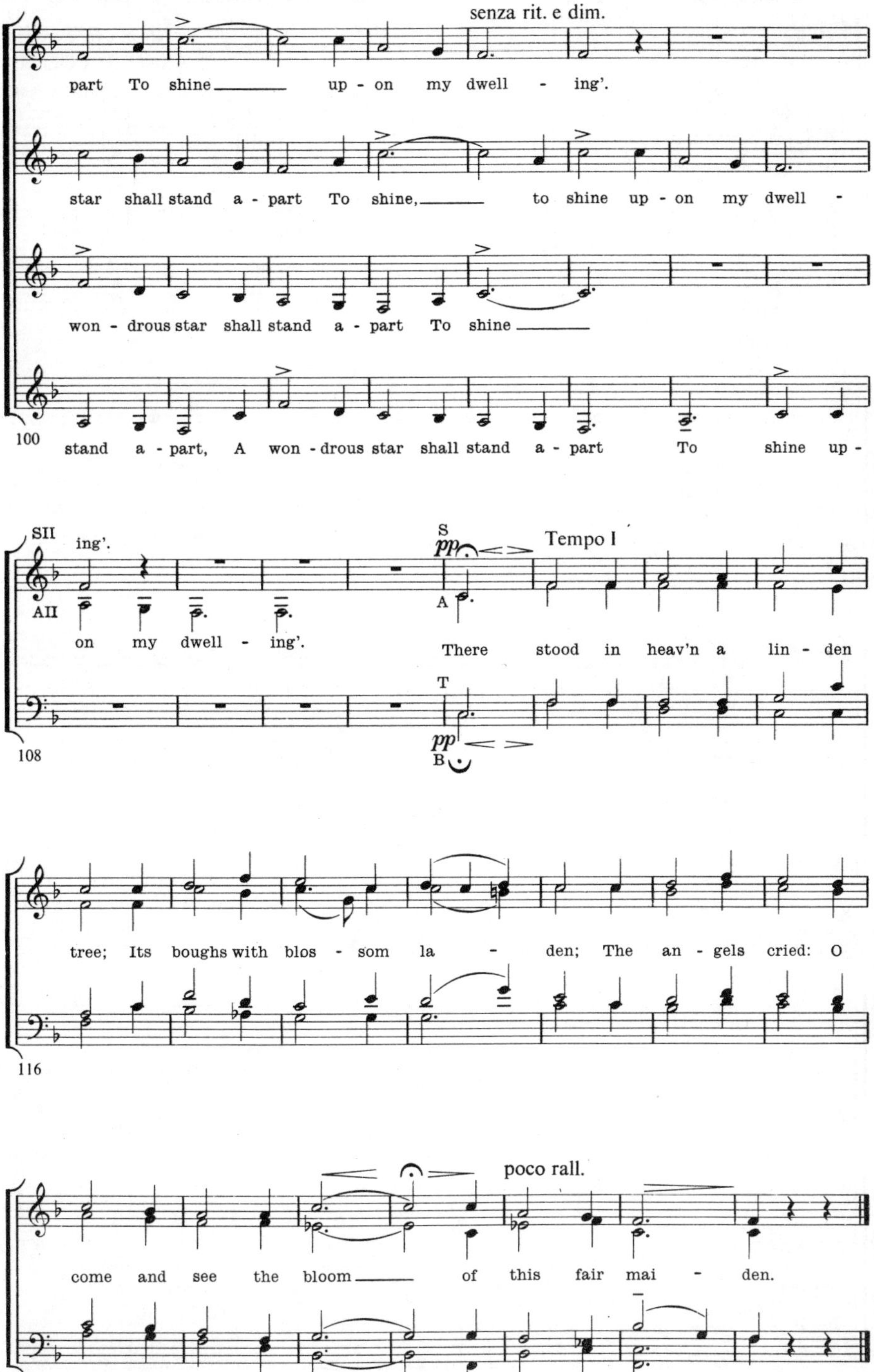

senza rit. e dim.

part To shine ——— up - on my dwell - ing'.

star shall stand a - part To shine, ——— to shine up - on my dwell -

won - drous star shall stand a - part To shine ———

100 stand a - part, A won - drous star shall stand a - part To shine up -

SII ing'.

AII on my dwell - ing'.

S *pp* Tempo I

A There stood in heav'n a lin - den

T

108

pp B

tree; Its boughs with blos - som la - den; The an - gels cried: O

116

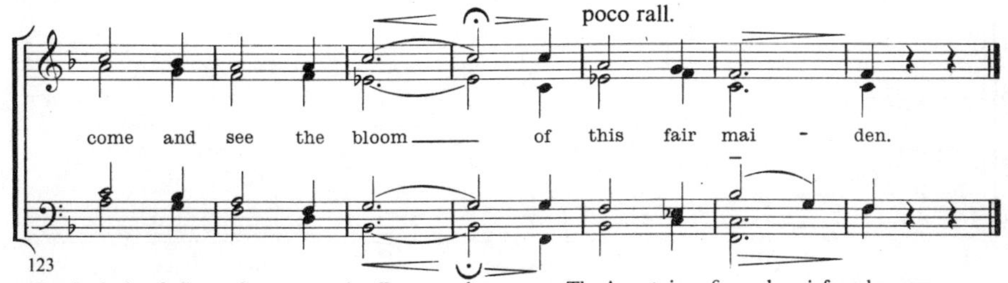

One-in-the-bar feeling and very expressive. Do not prolong pauses. The A parts in v. 6 may be reinforced or even replaced by T.

43

The Lord at first did Adam make

Words
TRADITIONAL

Music arr. by
ARNOLD COOKE

Allegretto (♩ = 120)

English tune

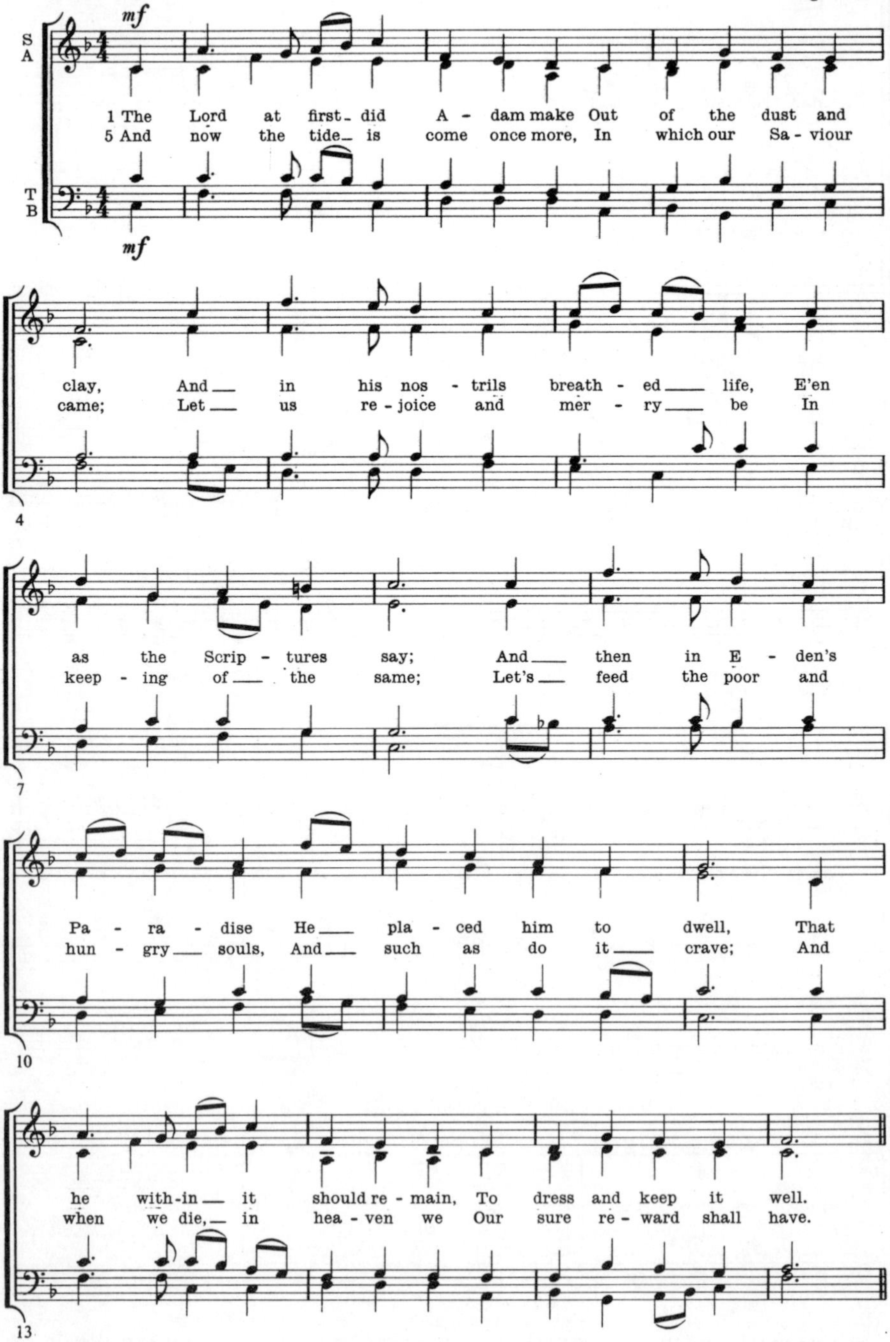
S
A
T
B
mf
1 The Lord at first-did A-dam make Out of the dust and
5 And now the tide-is come once more, In which our Sa-viour
mf
clay, And in his nos-trils breath-ed life, E'en
came; Let us re-joice and mer-ry be In
4
as the Scrip-tures say; And then in E-den's
keep-ing of the same; Let's feed the poor and
7
Pa-ra-dise He pla-ced him to dwell, That
hun-gry souls, And such as do it crave; And
10
he with-in it should re-main, To dress and keep it well.
when we die, in hea-ven we Our sure re-ward shall have.
13

REFRAIN
Now let good Christ-ians all be-gin Sin's e-vil ways to shun, And
17

to re-joice and mer-ry be, For Christ-mas is be-gun.
21
And to re-joice,

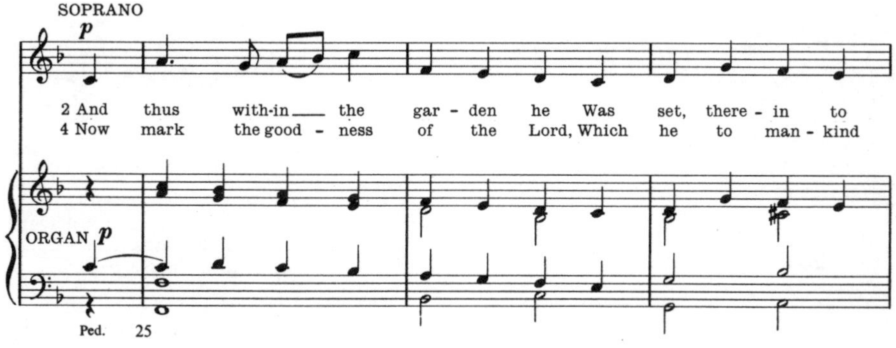
SOPRANO
2 And thus with-in the gar-den he Was set, there-in to
4 Now mark the good-ness of the Lord, Which he to man-kind
ORGAN
Ped. 25

stay; And in com-mand-ment un-to him These
bore; His mer-cy soon he did ex-tend, Lost
28

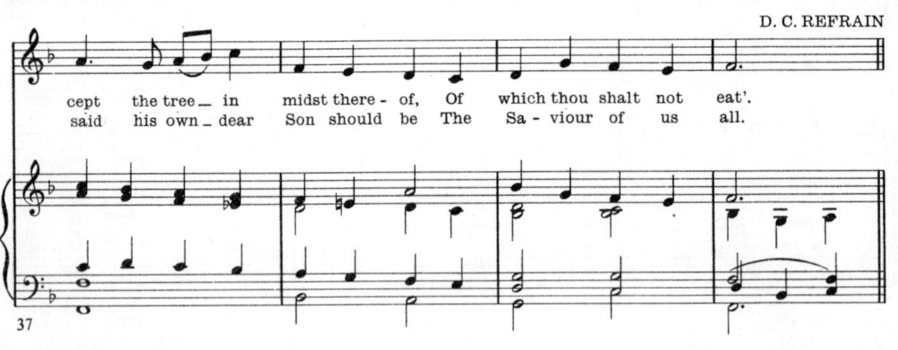

TENOR & BASS UNACCOMPANIED

Sing in a straightforward manner with shapely phrasing and keep a two-in-the-bar feeling. Ensure prominence of melody in v. 3. Adopt a sensible accentuation of the words.

44

There is no rose of such virtue

Words
MEDIEVAL

Music
JOHN JOUBERT Opus 14

mp
For in this rose con- tain - èd was Heav'n and earth in
mp
For in this rose con - tain - èd was Heav'n and earth in
mp
For in — this — rose con-tain - èd — was Heav'n and earth in
mp
For in — this — rose con-tain — èd — was Heav'n and earth in
mp
14
lit - tle space: Res mi-ran - da.
lit - tle — space: Res mi-ran - da.
lit - tle — space: Res mi - ran - da.
lit - tle space: Res mi - ran - da.
20

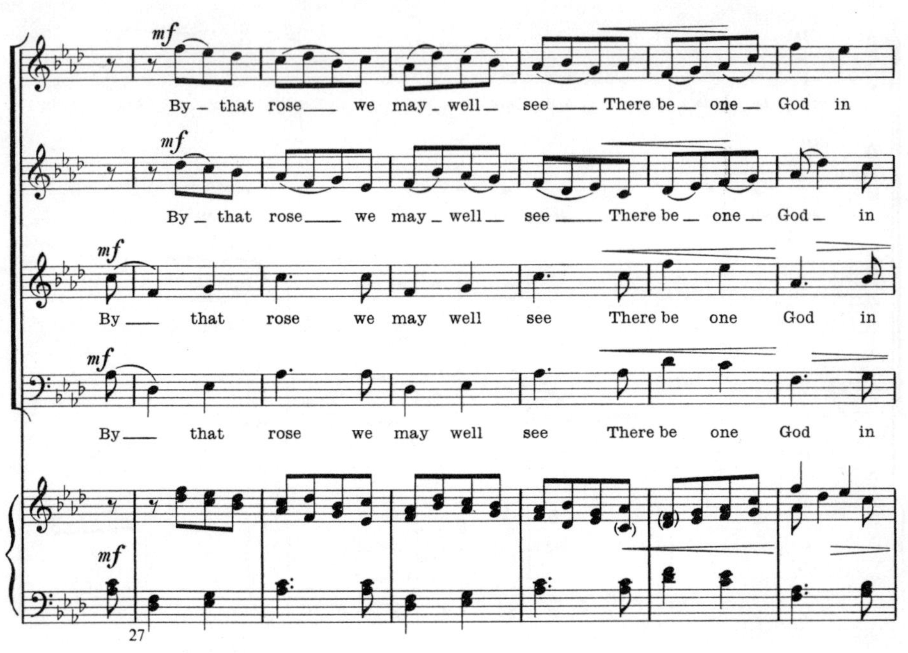

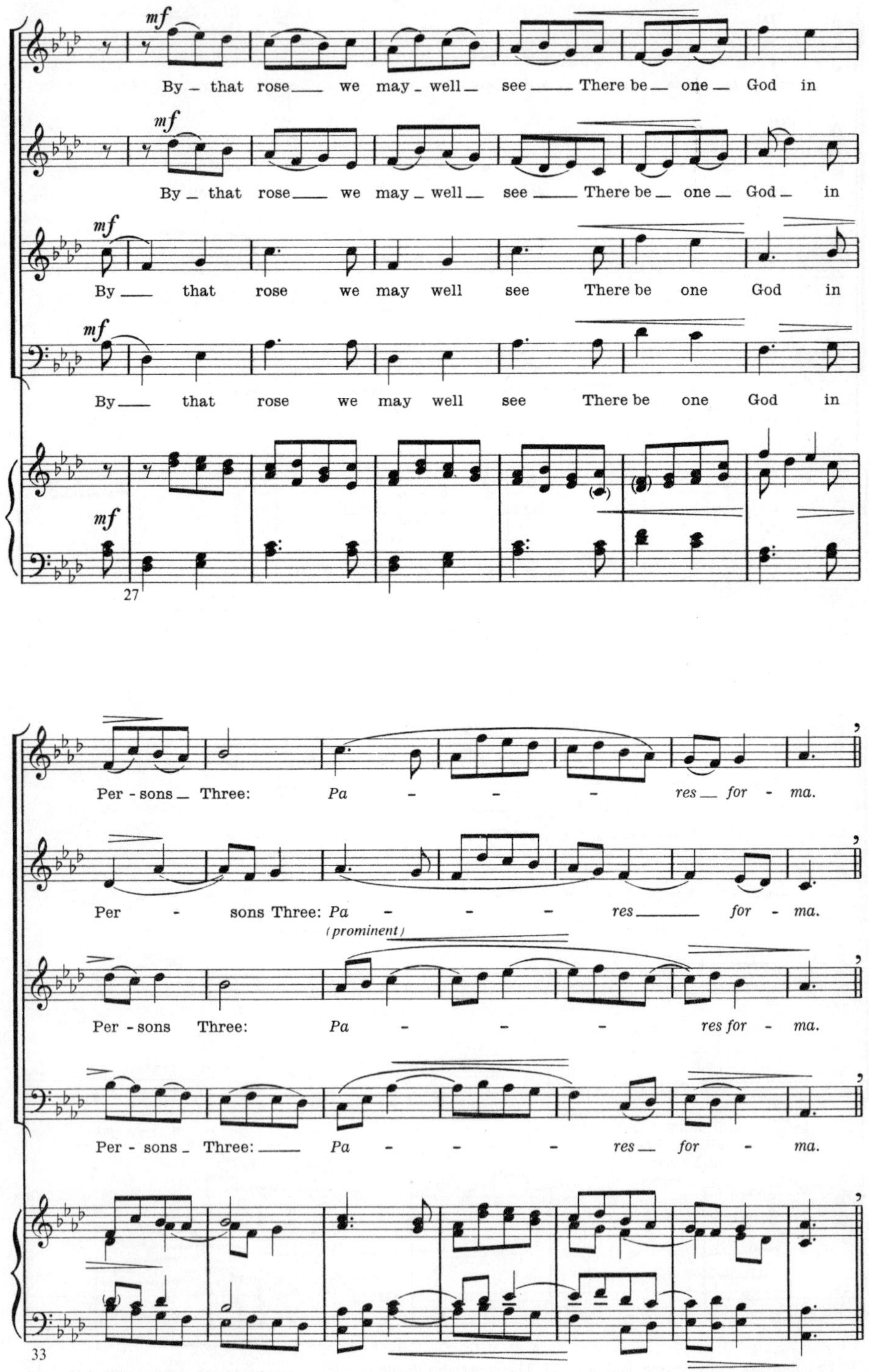
mf
By that rose we may well see There be one God in
By that rose we may well see There be one God in
By that rose we may well see There be one God in
By that rose we may well see There be one God in
27
Per - sons Three: Pa - - - res for - ma.
Per - sons Three: Pa - - - res for - ma.
(prominent)
Per - sons Three: Pa - - - res for - ma.
Per - sons Three: Pa - - - res for - ma.
33

poco più lento

p

Then leave we all this world - ly mirth And fol - low we this joy - ous

p

Then leave we all this world - ly mirth And fol - low we this joy - ous

poco più lento

p

40

lento rall.

pp

birth: *Tran - - - - se - a - mus.*

pp

birth: *Tran - - - - se - a - mus.*

pp

Tran - - - - se - a - mus.

pp

Tran - - - - se - a - mus.

lento rall.

pp

47

To be unhurried, easily flowing, and peaceful. The crescendos should be neither big nor sudden. Special care is needed to ensure unanimity when voices move in thirds.

45

Thou whom shepherds worshipped

(Quem pastores)

Words
GERMAN
(*English translation by C. S. Phillips*)*

Music arr. by
DESMOND RATCLIFFE
German tune

* By permission of the Proprietors of Hymns A & M

S
A
T
B
mf
Thou _ to whom _ came wise _ men
Ad _ quem ma - gi am - bu -
mf
mf
27
far - ing, Gold _ and myrrh _ and in - cense bear - ing,
la - bant, Au - rum, thus, _ myrr - ham _ por - ta - bant,
33
f
Heart - felt hom - age
Im - mo - la - bant
f
cresc.
f
38

thus de - clar - ing To the King that's born for all:
haec sin - cer - re Na - to re - gi glo - ri - ae.
44
50
cresc.
ff
Bend - ing low in a - dor - a - tion Thee we
Chris - to re - gi, De - o na - to, Per Ma -
ff
ff
58

Vocal line must flow gently with plenty of shape, and no harshness at *ff* climaxes.

46

'Twas in the year that King Uzziah died

Words
ISAIAH VI, 1-4
*(Adapted by G. R. Woodward)**

Music arr. by
GEOFFREY BUSH
Tune in the 5th Mode: a metrical form of the Sanctus

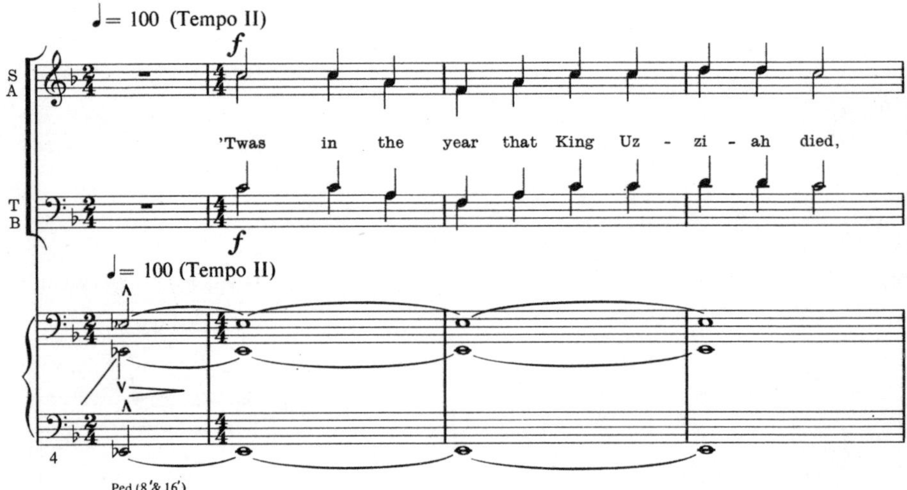

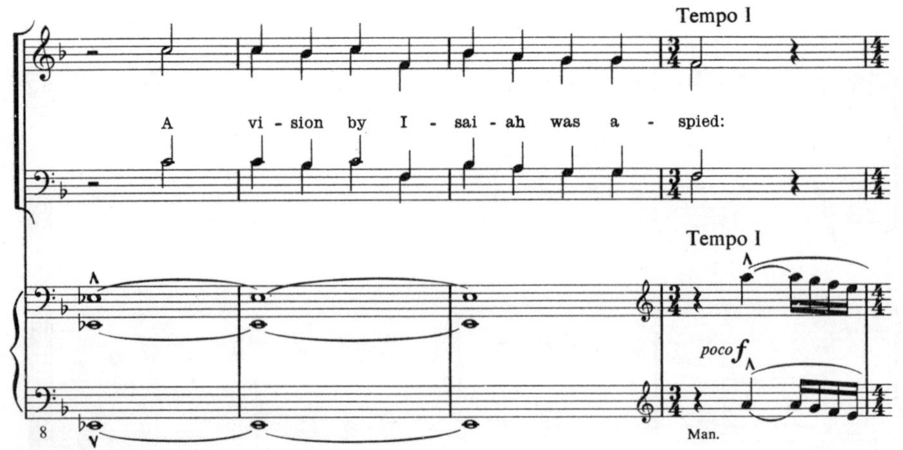

*From the Cambridge Carol Book by permission of the S.P.C.K.

tornando al Tempo II
tornando al Tempo II
12
Ped.
f
A lofty throne-the Lord was set there-on;
f
Tempo I Tempo II
Tempo I Tempo II
poco f
15
f
And with his glory all the temple shone.
f
19

Minim beat (𝅗𝅥 = ♩ of Tempo II)
SOPRANO(Semichorus) mf
Bright Se - ra - phim were stand-ing
TENOR(Semichorus)
mf
Minim beat (𝅗𝅥 = ♩ of Tempo II)
mp clear and unhurried
23
Man.
round a-bout. Six wings had ev-ery of that quire de-vout.
27
Ped.
Man.
With twain he awe - some veil'd his face, and so With twain he
poco a poco
31
Ped.
Man.

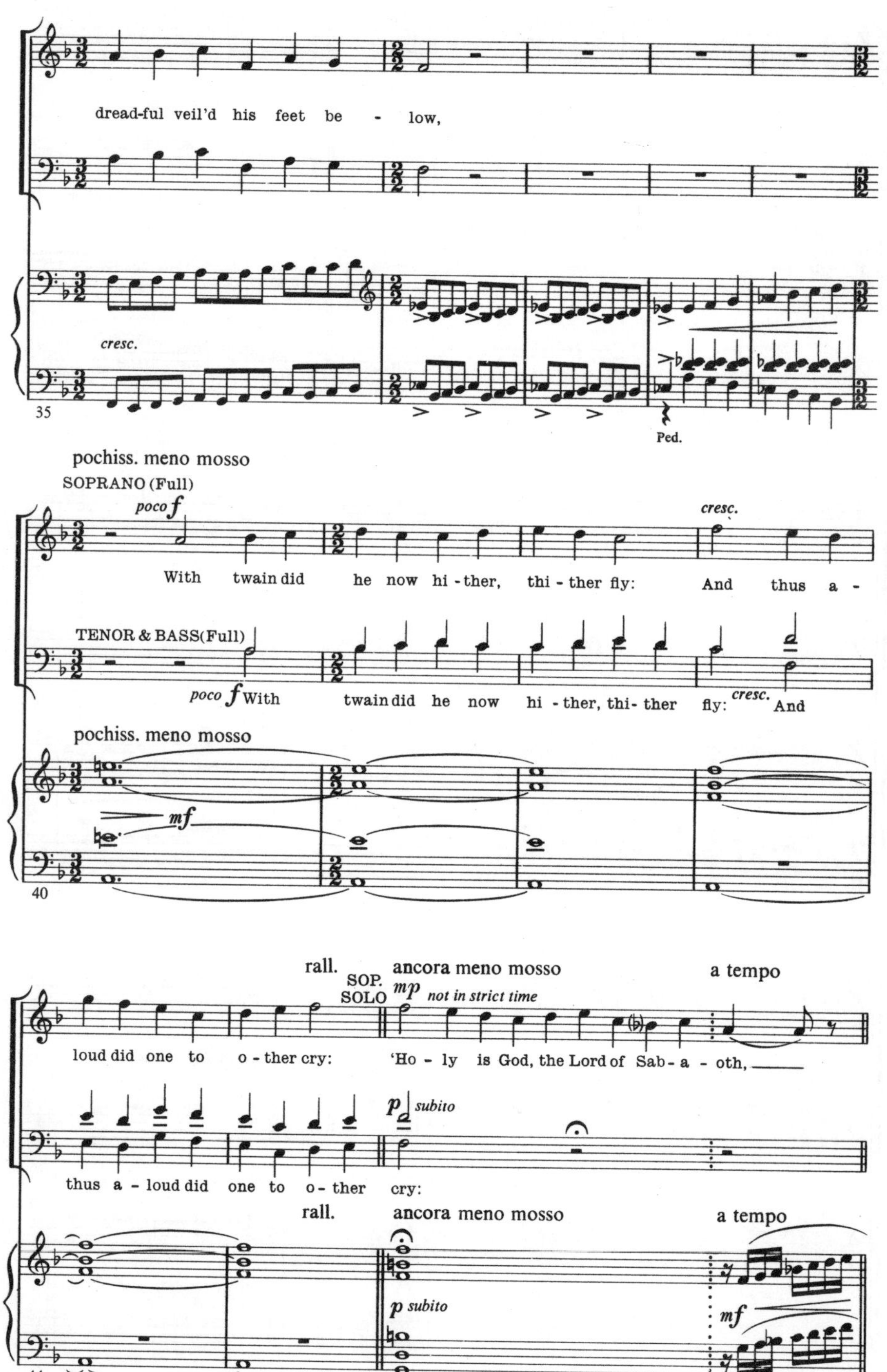
dread-ful veil'd his feet be - low,
cresc.
35
Ped.
pochiss. meno mosso
SOPRANO (Full)
poco f
With twain did he now hi - ther, thi - ther fly: And thus a -
cresc.
TENOR & BASS (Full)
poco f With twain did he now hi - ther, thi - ther fly: And
cresc.
pochiss. meno mosso
mf
40
rall.
ancora meno mosso
a tempo
SOP. SOLO
mp not in strict time
loud did one to o - ther cry: 'Ho - ly is God, the Lord of Sab - a - oth,
p subito
thus a - loud did one to o - ther cry:
rall.
ancora meno mosso
a tempo
p subito
mf
44
Man.

(crotchet beat)
ten.
A tempo come prima
mf TENOR SOLO not in strict time
Ho - ly is God, the Lord of Sab - a - oth,
(crotchet beat)
A tempo come prima
ten.
mf
cresc.
47
f
FULL
Ho - ly is God, the Lord of
FULL
f
f
Ped.
49
un poco largamente
Sab - a - oth, Full of his glo - ry, earth and hea - ven,
un poco largamente
52

The melody should be sung clearly and emphatically, without neglecting good phrasing and sensible verbal accentuation.

47

Until I wander'd

Words
HERBERT READ*

Music
ALAN RIDOUT

*From 'Moon's Farm' by permission of the author and the publishers, Faber & Faber Ltd

This needs delicacy and precise rhythm. Watch the staccato indications carefully.

48

Unto us is born a Son

Words
PIAE CANTIONES, 1582
(*English translation by G. R. Woodward*)

Music arr. by
THOMAS EASTWOOD
Tune from Piae Cantiones

Words from the Cowley Carol Book by permission of A. R. Mowbray & Co. Ltd.

ter - nal, Of lords the Lord e - ter - nal.
14
meno mosso
p tranquillo
Christ, from heav'n des - cend - ing low, Comes on earth a stran - ger:
p tranquillo
meno mosso (♩ = 120)
p (Sw.)
17 Man.
espress.
Ox and ass their own - er know Be - cra - dled in the
espress.
21

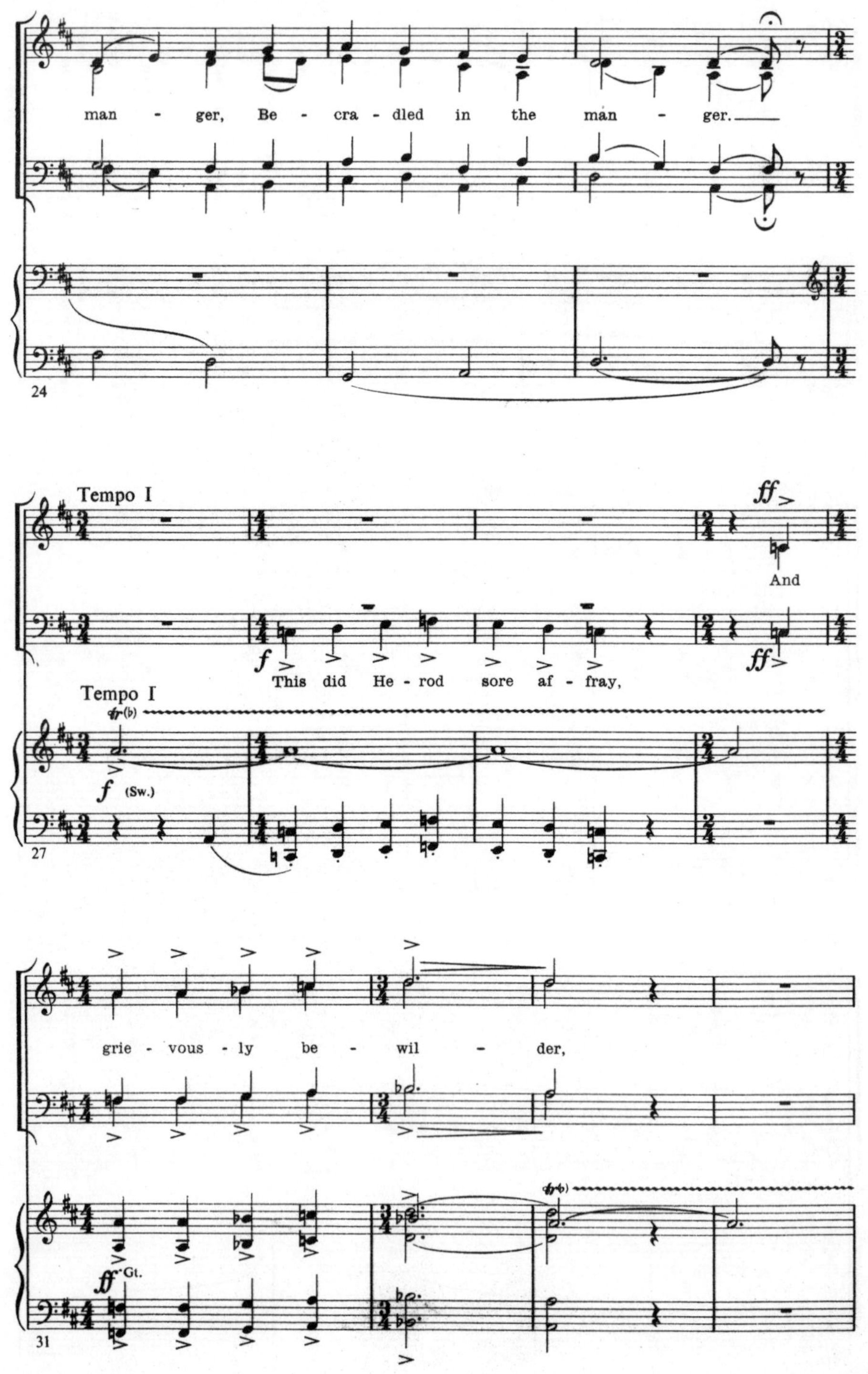

man - ger, Be - cra - dled in the man - ger.
24
Tempo I
ff
And
f
This did He - rod sore af - fray,
ff
Tempo I
f (Sw.)
27
grie - vous - ly be - wil - der,
ff Gt.
31

So he gave the word to slay,
feroce
ff
And slew the lit - tle
ff
feroce
f (Sw.)
f (Gt.)
ff (Gt.)
Ped.
35
molto riten.
Solo p triste
And slew the lit - tle child - er.
child - er,
molto riten.
p (Sw.)
Man.
39
Tempo II
SI mp dolce
Of his love and mer - cy mild This the Christ-mas
SII mp dolce
Of his love and mer - cy mild This the Christ-mas
Tempo II
43

*Sing D if E is found difficult.

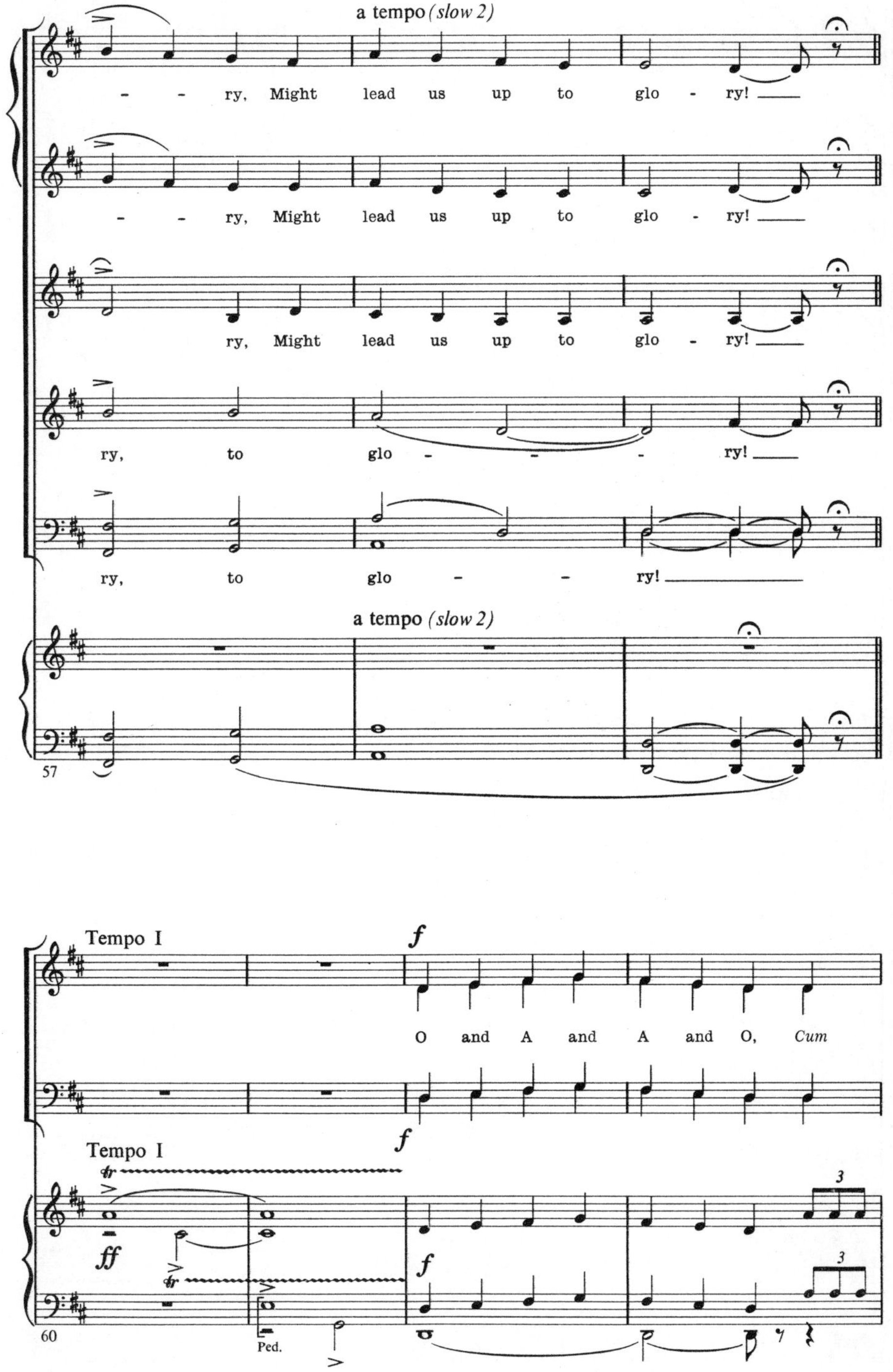

a tempo *(slow 2)*

- - ry, Might lead us up to glo - ry! ___

- - ry, Might lead us up to glo - ry! ___

ry, Might lead us up to glo - ry! ___

ry, to glo - - - ry! ___

ry, to glo - - ry! ___

a tempo *(slow 2)*

57

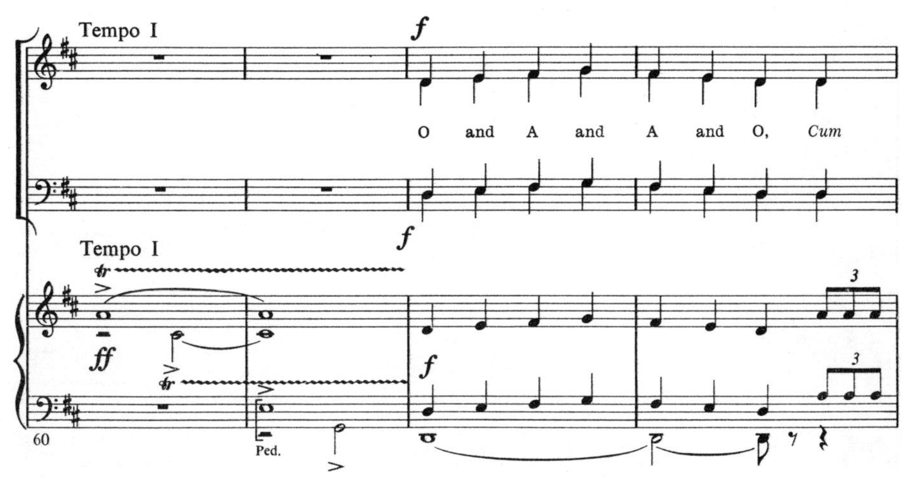

can - ti - bus in cho - ro,
Let our mer - ry
64
Be - ne - di - ca - mus Do - mi - no,
or - gan go,
Be -
Be - ne - di - ca - mus Do - mi - no,
67
Man.
ne - di - ca - mus Do - mi - no, Be - ne - di - ca - mus
70
Ped.

This calls for a dramatic interpretation. Ensure that the transition from section to section is effected easily, and that the style and tempo of each is set immediately.

49

We three Kings of Orient are

Words
J. H. HOPKINS, 1857

Music arr. by
RICHARD DRAKEFORD
Tune by J. H. Hopkins

MELCHIOR
Solo (or semichorus)
Born a King on Beth-le-hem's plain, Gold I bring, to crown Him a-gain,
pp
20
Man.
King for ev - er, ceas - ing nev - er, Ov - er us all to
24
Ped.
REFRAIN (Full)
p leggiero
reign.
O Star of won - der, star of night, Star with roy - al
p leggiero
27
poco
beau - ty bright, West - ward lead - ing, still pro - ceed - ing,
poco
31

Guide us to thy per - fect light.
34
Man.
CASPAR
Solo(or semichorus)
Frank - in - cense to of - fer have I, In - cense owns a De - i - ty nigh.
37
Prayer and prais - ing, all men rais - ing Wor - ship Him God most
41
REFRAIN (Full)
High. O Star of won - der, star of night,
44

Star with roy - al beau - ty bright, West - ward lead - ing,
47

still pro - ceed-ing, Guide us to thy per - fect light.
Solo
mp
50

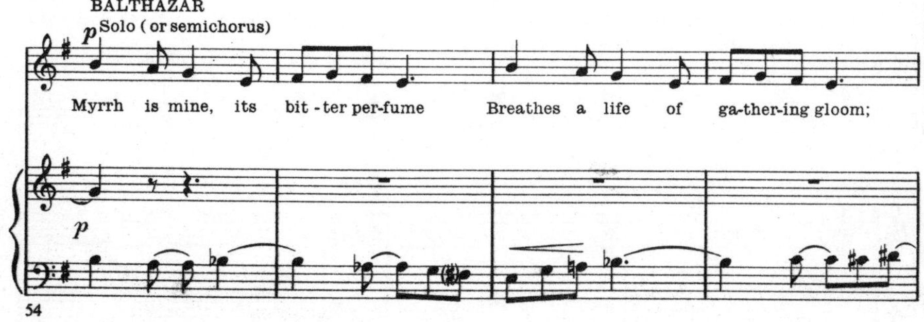
BALTHAZAR
Solo (or semichorus)
p
Myrrh is mine, its bit - ter per-fume Breathes a life of ga-ther-ing gloom;
p
54

Sorrow - ing, sigh - ing, bleed - ing, dy - ing, Sealed in the stone - cold
pp
(Man.)
58
REFRAIN
pp FULL
tomb. O Star of won - der, star of night, Star with roy - al
mp
Ped.
61
sempre. cresc.
beau - ty bright, West - ward lead - ing, still pro - ceed - ing,
molto cresc. poco a poco
65
f
Guide us to thy per - fect light.
f
68

Glo - rious now be - hold Him a - rise, King and
Glo - rious now be - hold Him a - rise, King and God and
Glo - rious now be - hold Him a - rise, King and
Glo - rious now be - hold Him a - rise, King and God and
71

God and sa - cri - fice, Heav'n sings Al - le - lu - ia,
sa - cri - fice, Heav'n sings Al - le - lu - ia, Al - le -
God and sa - cri - fice, Heav'n sings Al - le - lu - ia,
sa - cri - fice, Heav'n sings Al - le - lu - ia, Al - le -
74

Al - le - lu - ia the earth re - plies. Star of won - der,
lu - ia the earth re - plies. O Star of won - der,
Al - le - lu - ia the earth re - plies. Star of won - der,
lu - ia the earth re - plies. O Star of won - der,
ff
f
77

star of night, Star with roy - al beau - ty bright, West - ward lead - ing,
cresc.
80

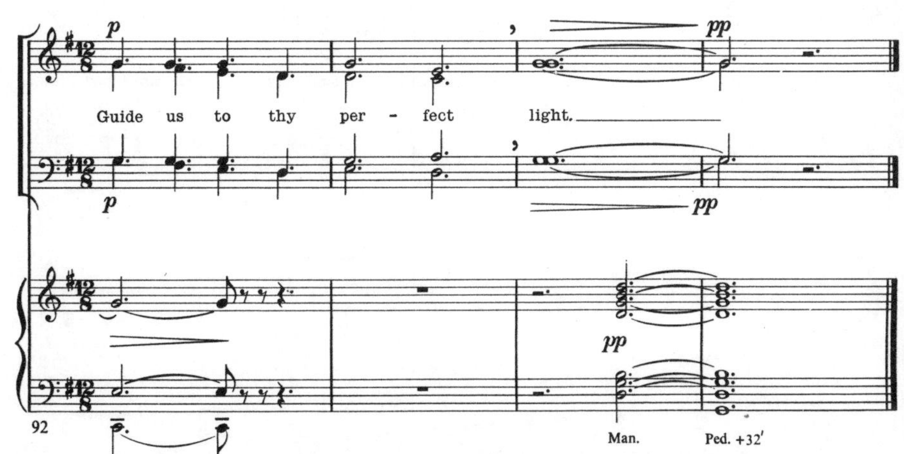

Avoid haste, and do not break the two-bar phrases into smaller units (e.g. 'westward leading', 'still proceeding'). If three soloists are used for the kings, choose voices of different timbre, i.e. TBarB.

50

What child is this

Words (*and* The old year now away is fled)

(a) TRADITIONAL
(b) 17th CENTURY

Music arr. by
ALAN RIDOUT

Tune: Greensleeves

Ma - ry!
Year.
mf espress.
16
2 Why lies He in such mean es - tate, Where
2 The name - day now of Christ we keep Who
19
ox and ass are feed - ing? Good Christ - ian, fear: for
for our sins did of - ten weep. His hands and feet were
22
sin - ners here The si - lent Word is plead - ing:
wound - ed deep And His bless - ed side with a spear.
pp
cresc.
Nails, spear, shall pierce Him through, The Cross be borne, for
His head they crown'd with thorns, And at Him did they
25
pp
cresc.
f
me, for you: Hail, hail, the Word made flesh, The
pour more scorn Whom for our soul was born; God
28
f
f espress.
Babe, the Son of Ma - ry! 3 So bring Him in - cense,
send you a Hap - py New Year. 3 And now with New Year's
f espress.
31

Keep flowing with a gentle lilt, avoiding undue emphasis on every dotted crotchet beat. The C♯ semiquaver in the 1st and 4th bars of each verse must be very light. Words must neatly fit the quavers, with sensible accentuation.

When Christ was born of Mary free

Words
ANON, 15th century

Music
JOHN GARDNER Opus 55

Note-values give only an approximate hint of the bouncing rhythm. Make sure that the choir feels this before applying polish. Can be performed in a variety of ways, but here is a suggestion: v. 1 SA, v. 2 TB, v. 3 SA, v. 4 Full. Is probably most effective sung by S only, in D or E.